OLD MOORE'S

HOROSCOPE AND ASTRAL DIARY

AQUARIUS

OLD MOORE'S

HOROSCOPE AND ASTRAL DIARY

AQUARIUS

foulsham
LONDON • NEW YORK • TORONTO • SYDNEY

W. Foulsham & Co. Ltd
for Foulsham Publishing Ltd
The Old Barrel Store, Drayman's Lane, Marlow, Bucks SL7 2FF

Foulsham books can be found in all good bookshops and direct from
www.foulsham.com

ISBN: 978-0-572-04632-3

Copyright © 2016 Foulsham Publishing Ltd

A CIP record for this book is available from the British Library

Printed in Denmark by Nørhaven, Viborg

CONTENTS

INTRODUCTION

Astrology has been a part of life for centuries now, and no matter how technological our lives become, it seems that it never diminishes in popularity. For thousands of years people have been gazing up at the star-clad heavens and seeing their own activities and proclivities reflected in the movement of those little points of light. Across centuries countless hours have been spent studying the way our natures, activities and decisions seem to be paralleled by their predictable movements. Old Moore, a time-served veteran in astrological research, continues to monitor the zodiac and has produced the Astral Diary for 2017, tailor-made to your own astrological makeup.

Old Moore's Astral Diary is unique in its ability to get the heart of your nature and to offer you the sort of advice that might come from a trusted friend. It enables you to see in a day-by-day sense exactly how the planets are working for you. The diary section advises how you can get the best from upcoming situations and allows you to plan ahead successfully. There's also room on each daily entry to record your own observations or appointments.

While other popular astrology books merely deal with your astrological 'Sun sign', the Astral Diaries go much further. Every person on the planet is unique and Old Moore allows you to access your individuality in a number of ways. The front section gives you the chance to work out the placement of the Moon at the time of your birth and to see how its position has set an important seal on your overall nature. Perhaps most important of all, you can use the Astral Diary to discover your Rising Sign. This is the zodiac sign that was appearing over the Eastern horizon at the time of your birth and is just as important to you as an individual as is your Sun sign.

It is the synthesis of many different astrological possibilities that makes you what you are and with the Astral Diaries you can learn so much. How do you react to love and romance? Through the unique Venus tables and the readings that follow them, you can learn where the planet Venus was at the time of your birth. It is even possible to register when little Mercury is 'retrograde', which means that it appears to be moving backwards in space when viewed from the Earth. Mercury rules communication, so be prepared to deal with a few setbacks in this area when you see the sign ☿. The Astral Diary will be an interest and a support throughout the whole year ahead.

Old Moore extends his customary greeting to all people of the Earth and offers his age-old wishes for a happy and prosperous period ahead.

THE ESSENCE OF AQUARIUS

Exploring the Personality of
Aquarius the Water Carrier

(21ST JANUARY – 19TH FEBRUARY)

What's in a sign?

Oh, what a wonderful person you can be! Despite a number of contradictions and one of the most complicated natures to be found anywhere in the zodiac, you certainly know how to make friends and influence people. Your ruling planet is Uranus, one of the more recently discovered members of the solar system's family. It rules modern communications, such as radio and television, and also has a response to the recent discoveries of science. It is within the world of 'the modern' that you reside and you have little or no difficulty keeping up with the ever-increasing pace of life.

People naturally like you and it's not surprising. You are open, liberal, and rarely judgmental, and you are often surrounded by deeply original and even eccentric types. Life to you is a storybook full of fascinating tales. Aquarians amass information 'on the hoof' and very little passes you by. Understanding what makes others tick is meat and drink to you and proves to be a source of endless joy. Unlike the other Air signs of Gemini and Libra, you are able to spend long hours on your own if necessary and always keep your mind active.

Aquarians have great creative potential; they are refined, often extremely well educated and they remain totally classless. This makes it easy for you to get on with just about any sort of person and also explains your general success in the material world. You are fascinating, original, thought-provoking and even quite deep on occasions. Matters that take months for others to synthesise, you can absorb in minutes. It is clear to everyone that you are one of life's natural leaders, but when you head any organisation you do so by co-operation and example because you are not in the least authoritarian.

In love you can be ardent and sincere – for a while at least. You need to be loved and it's true that deeply personal relationships can be a problem to you if they are not supplying what is most important to you. Few people know the real you, because your nature exists on so many different levels. For this reason alone you defy analysis and tend to remain outside the scope of orthodoxy. And because people can't weigh you up adequately, you appear to be more fascinating than ever.

Aquarius resources

Your chief resource has to be originality. Like a precious Fabergé Egg you are a single creation, unique and quite unlike anything else to be found anywhere in the world. Of course, used wrongly, this can make you seem odd or even downright peculiar. But Aquarians usually have a knack for creating the best possible impression. The chances are that you dress in your own way and speak the words that occur to you, and that you have a side to your nature that shuns convention. Despite this you know how to adapt when necessary. As a result your dinner parties would sport guests of a wide variety of types and stations. All of these people think they know the 'real you' and remain committed to helping you as much as they can.

The natural adaptability that goes along with being an Aquarian makes it possible for you to turn your hand to many different projects. And because you are from an Air sign, you can undertake a variety of tasks at the same time. This makes for a busy life, but being on the go is vital for you and you only tire when you are forced into jobs that you find demeaning, pointless or downright dull.

All of the above combines to make a nature that has 'resourcefulness' as its middle name. Arriving at a given set of circumstances – say a specific task that has to be undertaken – you first analyse what is required. Having done so you get cracking and invariably manage to impress all manner of people with your dexterity, attention to detail and downright intelligence. You can turn work into a social event, or derive financial gain from your social life. Activity is the keyword and you don't really differentiate between the various components of life as many people would.

Success depends on a number of different factors. You need to be doing things you enjoy as much you can and you simply cannot be held back or bound to follow rules that appear to make no sense to you. You respond well to kindness, and generally receive it because you are so considerate yourself. But perhaps your greatest skill of all is your ability to make a silk purse out of a sow's ear. You are never stuck for an idea and rarely let financial restrictions get in your way.

Beneath the surface

'What you see is what you get' could never really be considered a sensible or accurate statement when applied to the sign of Aquarius. It's difficult enough for you to know the way your complicated mind works, and almost impossible for others to sort out the tangle of possibilities. Your mind can be as untidy as a tatty workbox on occasions and yet at other times you can see through situations with a clarity that would dazzle almost any observer. It really depends on a whole host of circumstances, some of which are inevitably beyond your own control. You are at your best when you are allowed to take charge from the very start of any project, because then your originality of thought comes into play. Your sort of logic is unique to you, so don't expect anyone else to go down the same mental routes that you find easy to follow.

Aquarians are naturally kind and don't tend to discriminate. This is not a considered matter, it's simply the way you are. As a result it is very hard for you to understand prejudice, or individuals who show any form of intolerance. The fairness that you exemplify isn't something that you have to work at – it comes as naturally to you as breathing does.

You can be very peculiar and even a little cranky on occasions. These aspects of your nature are unlikely to have any bearing on your overall popularity, but they do betray a rather unusual mindset that isn't like that of any other zodiac sign. When you feel stressed you tend to withdraw into yourself, which is not really good for you. A much better strategy would be to verbalise what you are thinking, even though this is not always particularly easy to do.

There are many people in the world who think they know you well, but each and every one of them knows only one Aquarian. There are always more, each a unique individual and probably as much of a mystery to you as they would be to all your relatives and friends, that is if any of them suspected just how deep and mysterious you can be. Despite these facts, your mind is clear and concise, enabling you to get to the truth of any given situation almost immediately. You should never doubt your intuitive foresight and, in the main, must always back your hunches. It is rare indeed for you to be totally wrong about the outcome of any potential situation and your genuine originality of thought is the greatest gift providence has bestowed on you.

Making the best of yourself

Interacting with the world is most important to you. Although you can sometimes be a good deal quieter than the other Air signs of Gemini and Libra, you are still a born communicator, with a great need to live your life to the full. If you feel hemmed in or constrained by circumstances, you are not going to show your best face to family, friends or colleagues. That's why you must move heaven and earth to make certain that you are not tied down in any way. Maintaining a sense of freedom is really just a mental state to Aquarius but it is absolutely vital to your well-being.

As far as work is concerned you need to be doing something that allows you the room you need to move. Any occupation that means thinking on your feet would probably suit you fine. All the same you feel more comfortable in administrative surroundings, rather than getting your hands dirty. Any profession that brings change and variety on a daily basis would be best. You are a good team operator, and yet can easily lead from the front. Don't be frightened to show colleagues that you have an original way of looking at life and that you are an inveterate problem solver.

In terms of friendship you tend to be quite catholic in your choice of pals. Making the best of yourself means keeping things that way. You are not naturally jealous yourself but you do tend to attract friends who are. Make it plain that you can't tie yourself down to any one association, no matter how old or close it may be. At least if you do this nobody can suggest that they weren't warned when you wander off to talk to someone else. Personal relationships are a different matter, though it's hardly likely that you would live in the pocket of your partner. In any situation you need space to breathe, and this includes romantic attachments. People who know you well will not try to hem you in.

Don't be frightened to show your unconventional, even wild side to the world at large. You are a bold character, with a great deal to say and a natural warmth that could melt an iceberg. This is the way providence made you and it is only right to use your gifts to the full.

The impressions you give

You are not a naturally secretive person and don't hold back very much when it comes to speaking your mind. It might be suggested therefore that the external and internal Aquarian is more or less the same person. Although generally true, it has to be remembered that you have a multi-faceted nature and one that adapts quickly to changing circumstances. It is this very adaptability that sets you apart in the eyes of the world.

You often make decisions based on intuitive foresight and although many Aquarians are of above average intelligence, you won't always make use of a deep knowledge of any given situation. In essence you often do what seems right, though you tend to act whilst others are still standing around and thinking. This makes you good to have around in a crisis and convinces many of those looking on that you are incredibly capable, relaxed and confident. Of course this isn't always the case, but even a nervous interior tends to breed outward action in the case of your zodiac sign, so the world can be forgiven for jumping to the wrong conclusion.

People like you – there's no doubt about that. However, you must realise that you have a very upfront attitude, which on occasions is going to get you into trouble. Your occasional weirdness, rather than being a turn-off, is likely to stimulate the interest that the world has in you. Those with whom you come into contact invariably find your personality to be attractive, generous, high-spirited and refreshing. For all these reasons it is very unlikely that you would actually make many enemies, even if some folk are clearly jealous of the easy way you have with the world.

One of the great things about Aquarians is that they love to join in. As a result you may find yourself doing all sorts of things that others would find either difficult or frightening. You can be zany, wild and even mad on occasions, but these tendencies will only get you liked all the more. The world will only tire of you if you allow yourself to get down in the dumps or grumpy – a very rare state for Aquarius.

The way forward

In terms of living your life to the full it is probable that you don't need any real advice from an astrologer. Your confidence allows you to go places that would make some people shiver, whilst your intuitive foresight gives you the armoury you need to deal with a world that can sometimes seem threatening. Yet for all this you are not immune to mental turmoil on occasions, and probably spend rather too much time in the fast lane. It's good to rest, a fact that you need to remember the next time you find yourself surrounded by twenty-seven jobs, all of which you are trying to undertake at the same time.

The more the world turns in the direction of information technology, the happier you are likely to become. If others have difficulty in this age of computers, it's likely that you relish the challenges and the opportunities that these artificial intelligences offer. You are happy with New Age concepts and tend to look at the world with compassion and understanding. Despite the fact that you are always on the go, it's rare for you to be moving forward so fast that you forget either the planet that brought you to birth, or the many underprivileged people who inhabit parts of it. You have a highly developed conscience and tend to work for the good of humanity whenever you can.

You might not be constructed of the highest moral fibre known to humanity, a fact that sometimes shows when it comes to romantic attachments. Many Aquarians play the field at some time in their lives and it's certain that you need a personal relationship that keeps you mentally stimulated. Although your exterior can sometimes seem superficial, you have a deep and sensitive soul – so perhaps you should marry a poet, or at least someone who can cope with the twists and turns of the Aquarian mind. Aquarians who tie themselves down too early, or to the wrong sort of individual, invariable end up regretting the fact.

You can be deeply creative and need to live in clean and cheerful surroundings. Though not exactly a minimalist you don't like clutter and constantly need to spring-clean your home – and your mind. Living with others isn't difficult for you, in fact it's essential. Since you are so adaptable you fit in easily to almost any environment, though you will always ultimately stamp your own character onto it. You love to be loved and offer a great deal in return, even if you are occasionally absent when people need you the most. In essence you are in love with life and so perhaps you should not be too surprised to discover that it is very fond of you too.

AQUARIUS ON THE CUSP

O ld Moore is often asked how astrological profiles are altered for those people born at either the beginning or the end of a zodiac sign, or, more properly, on the cusps of a sign. In the case of Aquarius this would be on the 21st of January and for two or three days after, and similarly at the end of the sign, probably from the 17th to the 19th of February. In this year's Astral Diaries, once again, Old Moore sets out to explain the differences regarding cuspid signs.

The Capricorn Cusp – January 21st to 23rd

What really sets you apart is a genuinely practical streak that isn't always present in the sign of Aquarius when taken alone. You are likely to have all the joy of life and much of the devil-may-care attitude of your Sun sign, but at the same time you are capable of getting things done in a very positive way. This makes you likely to achieve a higher degree of material success and means that you ally managerial skills with the potential for rolling up your sleeves and taking part in the 'real work' yourself. Alongside this you are able to harness the naturally intuitive qualities of Aquarius in a very matter-of-fact way. Few people would have the ability to pull the wool over your eyes and you are rarely stuck for a solution, even to apparently difficult problems.

You express yourself less well than Aquarius taken alone, and you may have a sort of reserve that leads others to believe that your mind is full of still waters which run very deep. The air of mystery can actually be quite useful, because it masks an ability to react and move quickly when necessary, which is a great surprise to the people around you. However, there are two sides to every coin and if there is a slightly negative quality to this cuspid position it might lie in the fact that you are not quite the communicator that tends to be the case with Aquarius, and you could go through some fairly quiet and introspective phases that those around you would find somewhat difficult to understand. In a positive sense this offers a fairly wistful aspect to your nature that may, in romantic applications, appear very attractive. There is something deeply magnetic about your nature and it isn't quite possible for everyone to understand what makes you tick. Actually this is part of your appeal because there is nothing like curiosity on the part of others to enhance your profile.

Getting things done is what matters the most to you, harnessed to the ability to see the wider picture in life. It's true that not everyone understands your complex nature, but in friendship you are scarcely short of supportive types. Family members can be especially important to you and personal attachments are invariably made for life.

The Pisces Cusp – February 17th to 19th

It appears that you are more of a thinker than most and achieve depths of contemplation that would be totally alien to some signs of the zodiac. Much of your life is given over to the service you show for humanity as a whole but you don't sink into the depths of despair in the way that some Piscean individuals are inclined to do. You are immensely likeable and rarely stuck for a good idea. You know how to enjoy yourself, even if this quality is usually tied to the support and assistance that you constantly give to those around you.

Many of you will already have chosen a profession that somehow fulfils your need to be of service, and it isn't unusual for Pisces-cusp Aquarians to alter their path in life totally if it isn't fulfilling this most basic requirement. When necessary, you can turn your hand to almost anything, generally giving yourself totally to the task in hand, sometimes to the exclusion of everything else. People with this combination often have two very different sorts of career, sometimes managing to do both at the same time. Confidence in practical matters isn't usually lacking, even if you sometimes think that your thought processes are a little bit muddled.

In love you are ardent and more sincere than Aquarius sometimes seems to be. There can be a tinge of jealousy at work now and again in deep relationships, but you are less likely than Pisces to let this show. You tend to be very protective of the people who are most important in your life and these are probably fewer in number than often seems to be the case for Aquarius. Your love of humanity and the needs it has of you are of supreme importance and you barely let a day pass without offering some sort of assistance. For this reason, and many others, you are a much loved individual and show your most caring face to the world for the majority of your life. Material success can be hard to come by at first, but it isn't really an aspect of life that worries you too much in any case. It is far more important for you to be content with your lot and, if you are happy, it seems that more or less everything else tends to follow.

AQUARIUS AND ITS ASCENDANTS

The nature of every individual on the planet is composed of the rich variety of zodiac signs and planetary positions that were present at the time of their birth. Your Sun sign, which in your case is Aquarius, is one of the many factors when it comes to assessing the unique person you are. Probably the most important consideration, other than your Sun sign, is to establish the zodiac sign that was rising over the eastern horizon at the time that you were born. This is your Ascending or Rising sign. Most popular astrology fails to take account of the Ascendant, and yet its importance remains with you from the very moment of your birth, through every day of your life. The Ascendant is evident in the way you approach the world, and so, when meeting a person for the first time, it is this astrological influence that you are most likely to notice first. Our Ascending sign essentially represents what we appear to be, while the Sun sign is what we feel inside ourselves.

The Ascendant also has the potential for modifying our overall nature. For example, if you were born at a time of day when Aquarius was passing over the eastern horizon (this would be around the time of dawn) then you would be classed as a double Aquarian. As such, you would typify this zodiac sign, both internally and in your dealings with others. However, if your Ascendant sign turned out to be a Fire sign, such as Aries, there would be a profound alteration of nature, away from the expected qualities of Aquarius.

One of the reasons why popular astrology often ignores the Ascendant is that it has always been rather difficult to establish. Old Moore has found a way to make this possible by devising an easy-to-use table, which you will find on page 125 of this book. Using this, you can establish your Ascendant sign at a glance. You will need to know your rough time of birth, then it is simply a case of following the instructions.

For those readers who have no idea of their time of birth it might be worth allowing a good friend, or perhaps your partner, to read through the section that follows this introduction. Someone who deals with you on a regular basis may easily discover your Ascending sign, even though you could have some difficulty establishing it for yourself. A good understanding of this component of your nature is essential if you want to be aware of that 'other person' who is responsible for the way you make contact with the world at large. Your Sun sign, Ascendant sign, and the other pointers in this book will, together, allow you a far better understanding of what makes you tick as an individual. Peeling back the different layers of your astrological make-up can be an enlightening experience, and the Ascendant may represent one of the most important layers of all.

Aquarius with Aquarius Ascendant

You are totally unique and quite original, so much so that very few people could claim to understand what makes you tick. Routines get on your nerves and you need to be out there doing something most of the time. Getting where you want to go in life isn't too difficult, except that when you arrive, your destination might not look half so interesting as it did before. You are well liked and should have many friends. This is not to say that your pals have much in common with each other, because you choose from a wide cross-section of people. Although folks see you as being very reasonable in the main, you are capable of being quite cranky on occasions. Your intuition is extremely strong and is far less likely to let you down than would be the case with some individuals.

Travel is very important to you and you will probably live for some time in a different part of your own country, or even in another part of the world. At work you are more than capable, but do need something to do that you find personally stimulating, because you are not very good at constant routine. You can be relied upon to use your originality and find solutions that are instinctive and brilliant. Most people are very fond of you.

Aquarius with Pisces Ascendant

Here we find the originality of Aquarius balanced by the very sensitive qualities of Pisces, and it makes for a very interesting combination. When it comes to understanding other people you are second to none, but it's certain that you are more instinctive than either Pisces or Aquarius when taken alone. You are better at routines than Aquarius, but also relish a challenge more than the typical Piscean would. Active and enterprising, you tend to know what you want from life, but consideration of others, and the world at large, will always be part of the scenario. People with this combination often work on behalf of humanity and are to be found in social work, the medical profession and religious institutions. As far as beliefs are concerned you don't conform to established patterns, and yet may get closer to the truth of the Creator than many deep theological thinkers have ever been able to do. Acting on impulse as much as you do means that not everyone understands the way your mind works, but your popularity will invariably see you through.

Passionate and deeply sensitive, you are able to negotiate the twists and turns of a romantic life that is hardly likely to be run-of-the-mill. In the end, however, you should be able to discover a very deep personal and spiritual happiness.

Aquarius with Aries Ascendant

If ever anyone could be accused of setting off immediately, but slowly, it has to be you. These are very contradictory signs and the differences will express themselves in a variety of ways. One thing is certain, you have tremendous tenacity and will see a job through patiently from beginning to end, without tiring on the way and ensuring that every detail is taken care of properly. This combination often brings good health and a great capacity for continuity, particularly in terms of the length of life. You are certainly not as argumentative as the typical Aries, but you do know how to get your own way, which is just as well because you are usually thinking on behalf of everyone else and not just on your own account.

At home you can relax, which is a blessing for Aries, though in fact you seldom choose to do so because you always have some project or other on the go. You probably enjoy knocking down and rebuilding walls, though this is a practical tendency and not responsive to relationships, in which you are ardent and sincere. Impetuosity is as close to your heart as is the case for any type of subject, though you certainly have the ability to appear patient and steady. But it's just a front, isn't it?

Aquarius with Taurus Ascendant

There is nothing that you fail to think about deeply and with great intensity. You are wise, honest and very scientific in your approach to life. Routines are necessary in life but you have most of them sorted out well in advance and so always have time to look at the next interesting fact. If you don't spend all your time watching documentaries on the television set, you make a good friend and love to socialise. Most of the great discoveries of the world were probably made by people with this sort of astrological combination, though your nature is rather 'odd' on occasions and so can be rather difficult for others to understand.

You may be most surprised when others tell you that you are eccentric, but you don't really mind too much because for half of the time you are not inhabiting the same world as the rest of us. Because you can be delightfully dotty you are probably much loved and cherished by your friends, of which there are likely to be many. Family members probably adore you too, and you can be guaranteed to entertain anyone with whom you come into contact. The only fly in the ointment is that you sometimes lose track of reality, whatever that might be, and fly high in your own atmosphere of rarefied possibilities.

Aquarius with Gemini Ascendant

If you were around in the 1960s there is every chance that you were the first to go around with flowers in your hair. You are unconventional, original, quirky and entertaining. Few people would fail to notice your presence and you take life as it comes, even though on most occasions you are firmly in the driving seat. It all probability you care very much about the planet on which you live and the people with whom you share it. Not everyone understands you, but that does not really matter, for you have more than enough communication skills to put your message across intact. You should avoid wearing yourself out by worrying about things that you cannot control, and you definitely gain from taking time out to meditate. However, whether or not you allow yourself that luxury remains to be seen.

If you are not the most communicative form of Gemini subject then you must come a close second. Despite this fact much of what you have to say makes real sense and you revel in the company of interesting, intelligent and stimulating people, whose opinions on a host of matters will add to your own considerations. You are a true original in every sense of the word and the mere fact of your presence in the world is bound to add to the enjoyment of life experienced by the many people with whom you make contact.

Aquarius with Cancer Ascendant

The truly original spark, for which the sign of Aquarius is famed, can only enhance the caring qualities of Cancer, and is also inclined to bring the Crab out of its shell to a much greater extent than would be the case with certain other zodiac combinations. Aquarius is a party animal and never arrives without something interesting to say, which is doubly the case when the reservoir of emotion and consideration that is Cancer is feeding the tap. Your nature can be rather confusing for even you to deal with, but you are inspirational, bright, charming and definitely fun to be around.

The Cancer element in your nature means that you care about your home and the people to whom you are related. You are also a good and loyal friend, who would keep attachments for much longer than could be expected for Aquarius alone. You love to travel and can be expected to make many journeys to far-off places during your life. Some attention will have to be paid to your health, because you are capable of burning up masses of nervous energy, often without getting the periods of rest and contemplation that are essential to the deeper qualities of the sign of Cancer. Nevertheless you have determination, resilience and a refreshing attitude that lifts the spirits of the people in your vicinity.

Aquarius with Leo Ascendant

All associations with Aquarius bring originality, and you are no exception. You aspire to do your best most of the time but manage to achieve your objectives in an infinitely amusing and entertaining way. Not that you set out to do so, because if you are an actor on the stage of life, it seems as though you are a natural one. There is nothing remotely pretentious about your breezy personality or your ability to occupy the centre of any stage. This analogy is quite appropriate because you probably like the theatre. Being in any situation when reality is suspended for a while suits you down to the ground, and in any case you may regularly ask yourself if you even recognise what reality is. Always asking questions, both of yourself and the world at large, you soldier on relentlessly, though not to the exclusion of having a good time on the way.

Keeping to tried and tested paths is not your way. You are a natural trailblazer who is full of good ideas and who has the energy to put them into practice. You care deeply for the people who play an important part in your life but are wise enough to allow them the space they need to develop their own personalities along the way. Most people like you, many love you, and one or two think that you really are the best thing since sliced bread.

Aquarius with Virgo Ascendant

How could anyone make the convention unconventional? Well, if anyone can manage, you can. There are great contradictions here, because on the one hand you always want to do the expected thing, but the Aquarian quality within your nature loves to surprise everyone on the way. If you don't always know what you are thinking or doing, it's a pretty safe bet that others won't either, so it's important on occasions really to stop and think. However this is not a pressing concern, because you tend to live a fairly happy life and muddle through no matter what. Other people tend to take to you well and it is likely that you will have many friends. You tend to be bright and cheerful and can approach even difficult tasks with the certainty that you have the skills necessary to see them through to their conclusion. Give and take are important factors in the life of any individual and particularly so in your case. Because you can stretch yourself in order to understand what makes other people think and act in the way that they do, you have the reputation of being a good friend and a reliable colleague.

In love you can be somewhat more fickle than the typical Virgoan, and yet you are always interesting to live with. Where you are, things happen, and you mix a sparkling wit with deep insights.

Aquarius with Libra Ascendant

Stand by for a truly interesting and very inspiring combination here, but one that is sometimes rather difficult to fathom, even for the sort of people who believe themselves to be very perceptive. The reason for this could be that any situation has to be essentially fixed and constant in order to get a handle on it, and this is certainly not the case for the Aquarian–Libran type. The fact is that both these signs are Air signs, and to a certain extent as unpredictable as the wind itself.

To most people you seem to be original, frank, free and very outspoken. Not everything you do makes sense to others and if you were alive during the hippy era, it is likely that you went around with flowers in your hair, for you are a free-thinking idealist at heart. With age you mature somewhat, but never too much, because you will always see the strange, the comical and the original in life. This is what keeps you young and is one of the factors that makes you so very attractive to members of the opposite sex. Many people will want to 'adopt' you and you are at your very best when in company.

Much of your effort is expounded on others and yet, unless you discipline yourself a good deal, personal relationships of the romantic sort can bring certain difficulties. Careful planning is necessary.

Aquarius with Scorpio Ascendant

Here we have a combination that shows much promise and a flexibility that allows many changes in direction, allied to a power to succeed, sometimes very much against all the odds. Aquarius lightens the load of the Scorpio mind, turning the depths into potential, and intuitive foresight into a means for getting on in life. There are depths here, because even airy Aquarius isn't so easy to understand, and it is therefore a fact that some people with this combination will always be something of a mystery. However, even this fact can be turned to your advantage because it means that people will always be looking at you. Confidence is so often the key to success in life and the Scorpio–Aquarius mix offers this, or at least appears to do so. Even when this is not entirely the case, the fact that everyone around you believes it to be true is often enough.

You are usually good to know, and show a keen intellect and a deep intelligence, aided by a fascination for life that knows no bounds. When at your best you are giving, understanding, balanced and active. On those occasions when things are not going well for you, beware of a stubborn streak and the need to be sensational. Keep it light and happy and you won't go far wrong. Most of you are very, very much loved.

Aquarius with Sagittarius Ascendant

There is an original streak to your nature which is very attractive to the people with whom you share your life. Always different, ever on the go and anxious to try out the next experiment in life, you are interested in almost everything, and yet deeply attached to almost nothing. Everyone you know thinks that you are a little 'odd', but you probably don't mind them believing this because you know it to be true. In fact it is possible that you positively relish your eccentricity, which sets you apart from the common herd and means that you are always going to be noticed.

Although it may seem strange with this combination of Air and Fire, you can be distinctly cool on occasions, have a deep and abiding love of your own company now and again and won't be easily understood. Love comes fairly easily to you but there are times when you are accused of being self-possessed, self-indulgent and not willing enough to fall in line with the wishes of those around you. Despite this you walk on and on down your own path. At heart you are an extrovert and you love to party, often late into the night. Luxury appeals to you, though it tends to be of the transient sort. Travel could easily play a major and a very important part in your life.

Aquarius with Capricorn Ascendant

Here the determination of Capricorn is assisted by a slightly more adaptable quality and an off-beat personality that tends to keep everyone else guessing. You don't care to be quite so predictable as the archetypal Capricorn would be, and there is a more idealistic quality here, or at least one that shows more. A greater number of friends than Capricorn usually keeps is likely, though less than the true Aquarian would gather. Few people doubt your sincerity, though by no means all of them understand what makes you tick. Unfortunately you are not in a position to help them out, because you are not too sure yourself. All the same, you muddle through and can be very capable when the mood takes you.

Being a natural traveller, you love to see new places and would be quite fascinated by cultures that are very different to your own. People with this combination are inclined to spend some time living abroad and may even settle there. You look out for the underdog and will always have time for a good cause, no matter what it takes to help. In romantic terms you are a reliable partner, though with a slightly wayward edge which, if anything, tends to make you even more attractive. Listen to your intuition, which is well honed and rarely lets you down. Generally speaking you are very popular.

THE MOON AND THE PART IT PLAYS IN YOUR LIFE

In astrology the Moon is probably the single most important heavenly body after the Sun. Its unique position, as partner to the Earth on its journey around the solar system, means that the Moon appears to pass through the signs of the zodiac extremely quickly. The zodiac position of the Moon at the time of your birth plays a great part in personal character and is especially significant in the build-up of your emotional nature.

Sun Moon Cycles

The first lunar cycle deals with the part the position of the Moon plays relative to your Sun sign. I have made the fluctuations of this pattern easy for you to understand by means of a simple cyclic graph. It appears on the first page of each 'Your Month At A Glance', under the title 'Highs and Lows'. The graph displays the lunar cycle and you will soon learn to understand how its movements have a bearing on your level of energy and your abilities.

Your Own Moon Sign

Discovering the position of the Moon at the time of your birth has always been notoriously difficult because tracking the complex zodiac positions of the Moon is not easy. This process has been reduced to three simple stages with Old Moore's unique Lunar Tables. A breakdown of the Moon's zodiac positions can be found from page 28 onwards, so that once you know what your Moon Sign is, you can see what part this plays in the overall build-up of your personal character.

If you follow the instructions on the next page you will soon be able to work out exactly what zodiac sign the Moon occupied on the day that you were born and you can then go on to compare the reading for this position with those of your Sun sign and your Ascendant. It is partly the comparison between these three important positions that goes towards making you the unique individual you are.

HOW TO DISCOVER YOUR MOON SIGN

This is a three-stage process. You may need a pen and a piece of paper but if you follow the instructions below the process should only take a minute or so.

STAGE 1 First of all you need to know the Moon Age at the time of your birth. If you look at Moon Table 1, on page 26, you will find all the years between 1919 and 2017 down the left side. Find the year of your birth and then trace across to the right to the month of your birth. Where the two intersect you will find a number. This is the date of the New Moon in the month that you were born. You now need to count forward the number of days between the New Moon and your own birthday. For example, if the New Moon in the month of your birth was shown as being the 6th and you were born on the 20th, your Moon Age Day would be 14. If the New Moon in the month of your birth came after your birthday, you need to count forward from the New Moon in the previous month. If you were born in a Leap Year, remember to count the 29th February. You can tell if your birth year was a Leap Year if the last two digits can be divided by four. Whatever the result, jot this number down so that you do not forget it.

STAGE 2 Take a look at Moon Table 2 on page 27. Down the left hand column look for the date of your birth. Now trace across to the month of your birth. Where the two meet you will find a letter. Copy this letter down alongside your Moon Age Day.

STAGE 3 Moon Table 3 on page 27 will supply you with the zodiac sign the Moon occupied on the day of your birth. Look for your Moon Age Day down the left hand column and then for the letter you found in Stage 2. Where the two converge you will find a zodiac sign and this is the sign occupied by the Moon on the day that you were born.

Your Zodiac Moon Sign Explained

You will find a profile of all zodiac Moon Signs on pages 28 to 31, showing in yet another way how astrology helps to make you into the individual that you are. In each daily entry of the Astral Diary you can find the zodiac position of the Moon for every day of the year. This also allows you to discover your lunar birthdays. Since the Moon passes through all the signs of the zodiac in about a month, you can expect something like twelve lunar birthdays each year. At these times you are likely to be emotionally steady and able to make the sort of decisions that have real, lasting value.

Moon Table 1

YEAR	DEC	JAN	FEB	YEAR	DEC	JAN	FEB	YEAR	DEC	JAN	FEB
1919	21	1/31	–	1952	17	26	25	1985	12	21	19
1920	10	20	19	1953	6	15	14	1986	1/30	10	9
1921	29	9	8	1954	25	5	3	1987	20	29	28
1922	18	27	26	1955	14	24	22	1988	9	19	17
1923	8	17	15	1956	2	13	11	1989	28	7	6
1924	26	6	5	1957	21	1/30	–	1990	17	26	25
1925	15	24	23	1958	10	19	18	1991	6	15	14
1926	5	14	12	1959	29	9	7	1992	24	4	3
1927	24	3	2	1960	18	27	26	1993	14	23	22
1928	12	21	19	1961	7	16	15	1994	2	11	10
1929	1/30	11	9	1962	26	6	5	1995	22	1/30	–
1930	19	29	28	1963	15	25	23	1996	10	20	18
1931	9	18	17	1964	4	14	13	1997	28	9	7
1932	27	7	6	1965	22	3	1	1998	18	27	26
1933	17	25	24	1966	12	21	19	1999	7	17	16
1934	6	15	14	1967	1/30	10	9	2000	26	6	4
1935	25	5	3	1968	20	29	28	2001	15	25	23
1936	13	24	22	1969	9	19	17	2002	4	13	12
1937	2	12	11	1970	28	7	6	2003	23	3	1
1938	21	1/31	–	1971	17	26	25	2004	11	21	20
1939	10	20	19	1972	6	15	14	2005	30	10	9
1940	28	9	8	1973	25	5	4	2006	20	29	28
1941	18	27	26	1974	14	24	22	2007	9	18	16
1942	8	16	15	1975	3	12	11	2008	27	8	6
1943	27	6	4	1976	21	1/31	29	2009	16	26	25
1944	15	25	24	1977	10	19	18	2010	6	15	14
1945	4	14	12	1978	29	9	7	2011	25	4	3
1946	23	3	2	1979	18	27	26	2012	12	23	22
1947	12	21	19	1980	7	16	15	2013	2	12	10
1948	1/30	11	9	1981	26	6	4	2014	2	1/31	–
1949	19	29	27	1982	15	25	23	2015	20	19	20
1950	9	18	16	1983	4	14	13	2016	29	9	8
1951	28	7	6	1984	22	3	1	2017	18	27	25

Table 2

DAY	JAN	FEB
1	A	D
2	A	D
3	A	D
4	A	D
5	A	D
6	A	D
7	A	D
8	A	D
9	A	D
10	A	E
11	B	E
12	B	E
13	B	E
14	B	E
15	B	E
16	B	E
17	B	E
18	B	E
19	B	E
20	B	F
21	C	F
22	C	F
23	C	F
24	C	F
25	C	F
26	C	F
27	C	F
28	C	F
29	C	F
30	C	–
31	D	–

Table 3

M/D	A	B	C	D	E	F	G
0	CP	AQ	AQ	AQ	PI	PI	PI
1	AQ	AQ	AQ	PI	PI	PI	AR
2	AQ	AQ	PI	PI	PI	AR	AR
3	AQ	PI	PI	PI	AR	AR	AR
4	PI	PI	AR	AR	AR	AR	TA
5	PI	AR	AR	AR	TA	TA	TA
6	AR	AR	AR	TA	TA	TA	GE
7	AR	AR	TA	TA	TA	GE	GE
8	AR	TA	TA	TA	GE	GE	GE
9	TA	TA	GE	GE	GE	CA	CA
10	TA	GE	GE	GE	CA	CA	CA
11	GE	GE	GE	CA	CA	CA	LE
12	GE	GE	CA	CA	CA	LE	LE
13	GE	CA	CA	LE	LE	LE	LE
14	CA	CA	LE	LE	LE	VI	VI
15	CA	LE	LE	LE	VI	VI	VI
16	LE	LE	LE	VI	VI	VI	LI
17	LE	LE	VI	VI	VI	LI	LI
18	LE	VI	VI	VI	LI	LI	LI
19	VI	VI	VI	LI	LI	LI	SC
20	VI	LI	LI	LI	SC	SC	SC
21	LI	LI	LI	SC	SC	SC	SA
22	LI	LI	SC	SC	SC	SA	SA
23	LI	SC	SC	SC	SA	SA	SA
24	SC	SC	SC	SA	SA	SA	CP
25	SC	SA	SA	SA	CP	CP	CP
26	SA	SA	SA	CP	CP	CP	AQ
27	SA	SA	CP	CP	AQ	AQ	AQ
28	SA	CP	CP	AQ	AQ	AQ	AQ
29	CP	CP	CP	AQ	AQ	AQ	PI

AR = Aries, TA = Taurus, GE = Gemini, CA = Cancer, LE = Leo, VI = Virgo, LI = Libra, SC = Scorpio, SA = Sagittarius, CP = Capricorn, AQ = Aquarius, PI = Pisces

MOON SIGNS

Moon in Aries

You have a strong imagination, courage, determination and a desire to do things in your own way and forge your own path through life.

Originality is a key attribute; you are seldom stuck for ideas although your mind is changeable and you could take the time to focus on individual tasks. Often quick-tempered, you take orders from few people and live life at a fast pace. Avoid health problems by taking regular time out for rest and relaxation.

Emotionally, it is important that you talk to those you are closest to and work out your true feelings. Once you discover that people are there to help, there is less necessity for you to do everything yourself.

Moon in Taurus

The Moon in Taurus gives you a courteous and friendly manner, which means you are likely to have many friends.

The good things in life mean a lot to you, as Taurus is an Earth sign that delights in experiences which please the senses. Hence you are probably a lover of good food and drink, which may in turn mean you need to keep an eye on the bathroom scales, especially as looking good is also important to you.

Emotionally you are fairly stable and you stick by your own standards. Taureans do not respond well to change. Intuition also plays an important part in your life.

Moon in Gemini

You have a warm-hearted character, sympathetic and eager to help others. At times reserved, you can also be articulate and chatty: this is part of the paradox of Gemini, which always brings duplicity to the nature. You are interested in current affairs, have a good intellect, and are good company and likely to have many friends. Most of your friends have a high opinion of you and would be ready to defend you should the need arise. However, this is usually unnecessary, as you are quite capable of defending yourself in any verbal confrontation.

Travel is important to your inquisitive mind and you find intellectual stimulus in mixing with people from different cultures. You also gain much from reading, writing and the arts but you do need plenty of rest and relaxation in order to avoid fatigue.

Moon in Cancer

The Moon in Cancer at the time of birth is a fortunate position as Cancer is the Moon's natural home. This means that the qualities of compassion and understanding given by the Moon are especially enhanced in your nature, and you are friendly and sociable and cope well with emotional pressures. You cherish home and family life, and happily do the domestic tasks. Your surroundings are important to you and you hate squalor and filth. You are likely to have a love of music and poetry.

Your basic character, although at times changeable like the Moon itself, depends on symmetry. You aim to make your surroundings comfortable and harmonious, for yourself and those close to you.

Moon in Leo

The best qualities of the Moon and Leo come together to make you warmhearted, fair, ambitious and self-confident. With good organisational abilities, you invariably rise to a position of responsibility in your chosen career. This is fortunate as you don't enjoy being an 'also-ran' and would rather be an important part of a small organisation than a menial in a large one.

You should be lucky in love, and happy, provided you put in the effort to make a comfortable home for yourself and those close to you. It is likely that you will have a love of pleasure, sport, music and literature. Life brings you many rewards, most of them as a direct result of your own efforts, although you may be luckier than average and ready to make the best of any situation.

Moon in Virgo

You are endowed with good mental abilities and a keen receptive memory, but you are never ostentatious or pretentious. Naturally quite reserved, you still have many friends, especially of the opposite sex. Marital relationships must be discussed carefully and worked at so that they remain harmonious, as personal attachments can be a problem if you do not give them your full attention.

Talented and persevering, you possess artistic qualities and are a good homemaker. Earning your honours through genuine merit, you work long and hard towards your objectives but show little pride in your achievements. Many short journeys will be undertaken in your life.

Moon in Libra

With the Moon in Libra you are naturally popular and make friends easily. People like you, probably more than you realise, you bring fun to a party and are a natural diplomat. For all its good points, Libra is not the most stable of astrological signs and, as a result, your emotions can be a little unstable too. Therefore, although the Moon in Libra is said to be good for love and marriage, your Sun sign and Rising sign will have an important effect on your emotional and loving qualities.

You must remember to relate to others in your decision-making. Co-operation is crucial because Libra represents the 'balance' of life that can only be achieved through harmonious relationships. Conformity is not easy for you because Libra, an Air sign, likes its independence.

Moon in Scorpio

Some people might call you pushy. In fact, all you really want to do is to live life to the full and protect yourself and your family from the pressures of life. Take care to avoid giving the impression of being sarcastic or impulsive and use your energies wisely and constructively.

You have great courage and you invariably achieve your goals by force of personality and sheer effort. You are fond of mystery and are good at predicting the outcome of situations and events. Travel experiences can be beneficial to you.

You may experience problems if you do not take time to examine your motives in a relationship, and also if you allow jealousy, always a feature of Scorpio, to cloud your judgement.

Moon in Sagittarius

The Moon in Sagittarius helps to make you a generous individual with humanitarian qualities and a kind heart. Restlessness may be intrinsic as your mind is seldom still. Perhaps because of this, you have a need for change that could lead you to several major moves during your adult life. You are not afraid to stand your ground when you know your judgement is right, you speak directly and have good intuition.

At work you are quick, efficient and versatile and so you make an ideal employee. You need work to be intellectually demanding and do not enjoy tedious routines.

In relationships, you anger quickly if faced with stupidity or deception, though you are just as quick to forgive and forget. Emotionally, there are times when your heart rules your head.

Moon in Capricorn

The Moon in Capricorn makes you popular and likely to come into the public eye in some way. The watery Moon is not entirely comfortable in the Earth sign of Capricorn and this may lead to some difficulties in the early years of life. An initial lack of creative ability and indecision must be overcome before the true qualities of patience and perseverance inherent in Capricorn can show through.

You have good administrative ability and are a capable worker, and if you are careful you can accumulate wealth. But you must be cautious and take professional advice in partnerships, as you are open to deception. You may be interested in social or welfare work, which suit your organisational skills and sympathy for others.

Moon in Aquarius

The Moon in Aquarius makes you an active and agreeable person with a friendly, easy-going nature. Sympathetic to the needs of others, you flourish in a laid-back atmosphere. You are broad-minded, fair and open to suggestion, although sometimes you have an unconventional quality which others can find hard to understand.

You are interested in the strange and curious, and in old articles and places. You enjoy trips to these places and gain much from them. Political, scientific and educational work interests you and you might choose a career in science or technology.

Money-wise, you make gains through innovation and concentration and Lunar Aquarians often tackle more than one job at a time. In love you are kind and honest.

Moon in Pisces

You have a kind, sympathetic nature, somewhat retiring at times, but you always take account of others' feelings and help when you can.

Personal relationships may be problematic, but as life goes on you can learn from your experiences and develop a better understanding of yourself and the world around you.

You have a fondness for travel, appreciate beauty and harmony and hate disorder and strife. You may be fond of literature and would make a good writer or speaker yourself. You have a creative imagination and may come across as an incurable romantic. You have strong intuition, maybe bordering on a mediumistic quality, which sets you apart from the mass. You may not be rich in cash terms, but your personal gifts are worth more than gold.

AQUARIUS IN LOVE

Discover how compatible in love you are with people from the same and other signs of the zodiac. Five stars equals a match made in heaven!

Aquarius meets Aquarius

This is a good match for several reasons. Most importantly, although it sounds arrogant, Aquarians like themselves. At its best, Aquarius is one of the fairest, most caring and genuinely pleasant zodiac signs and so it is only when faced by the difficulties created by others that it shows a less favourable side. Put two Aquarians together and voilà – instant success! Personal and family life should bring more joy. On the whole, a platform for adventure based on solid foundations. Star rating: * * * * *

Aquarius meets Pisces

Zodiac signs that follow each other often have something in common, but this is not the case with Aquarius and Pisces. Both signs are deeply caring, but in different ways. Pisces is one of the deepest zodiac signs, and Aquarius simply isn't prepared to embark on the journey. Pisceans, meanwhile, would probably find Aquarians superficial and even flippant. On the positive side there is potential for a well-balanced relationship, but unless one party is untypical of their zodiac sign, it often doesn't get started. Star rating: * *

Aquarius meets Aries

Aquarius is an Air sign, and Air and Fire often work well together, but not in the case of Aries and Aquarius. The average Aquarian lives in what the Ram sees as a fantasy world, so a meeting of minds is unlikely. Of course, the dominant side of Aries could be trained by the devil-may-care attitude of Aquarius. There are meeting points but they are difficult to establish. However, given sufficient time and an open mind on both sides, a degree of happiness is possible. Star rating: * *

Aquarius meets Taurus

In any relationship of which Aquarius is a part, surprises abound. It is difficult for Taurus to understand the soul-searching, adventurous, changeable Aquarian, but on the positive side, the Bull is adaptable and can respond well to a dose of excitement. Aquarians are kind and react well to the same quality coming back at them. Both are friendly, capable of deep affection and basically creative. Unfortunately, Taurus simply doesn't know what makes Aquarius tick, which could lead to feelings of isolation, even if these don't always show on the surface. Star rating: **

Aquarius meets Gemini

Aquarius is commonly mistaken for a Water sign, but in fact it's ruled by the Air element, and this is the key to its compatibility with Gemini. Both signs mix freely socially, and each has an insatiable curiosity. There is plenty of action, lots of love, but very little rest, and so great potential for success if they don't wear each other out! Aquarius revels in its own eccentricity, and encourages Gemini to emulate this. Theirs will be an unconventional household, but almost everyone warms to this crazy and unpredictable couple. Star rating: *****

Aquarius meets Cancer

Cancer is often attracted to Aquarius and, as Aquarius is automatically on the side of anyone who fancies it, so there is the potential for something good here. Cancer loves Aquarius' devil-may-care approach to life, but also recognises and seeks to strengthen the basic lack of self-confidence that all Air signs try so hard to keep secret. Both signs are natural travellers and are quite adventurous. Their family life could be unusual, but friends would recognise a caring, sharing household with many different interests shared by people genuinely in love. Star rating: ***

Aquarius meets Leo

The problem here is that Aquarius doesn't think in the general sense of the word, it knows. Leo, on the other hand, is more practical and relies more on logical reasoning, and consequently it doesn't understand Aquarius very well. Aquarians can also appear slightly frosty in their appreciation of others and this, too, will annoy Leo. This is a good match for a business partnership because Aquarius is astute, while Leo is brave, but personally the prognosis is less promising. Tolerance, understanding and forbearance are all needed to make this work. Star rating: **

Aquarius meets Virgo

Aquarius is a strange sign because no matter how well one knows it, it always manages to surprise. For this reason, against the odds, it's quite likely that Aquarius will form a sucessful relationship with Virgo. Aquarius is changeable, unpredictable and often quite odd, while Virgo is steady, a fuss-pot and very practical. Herein lies the key. What one sign needs, the other provides and that may be the surest recipe for success imaginable. On-lookers may not know why the couple are happy, but they will recognise that this is the case. Star rating: ****

Aquarius meets Libra

One of the best combinations imaginable, partly because both are Air signs and so share a common meeting point. But perhaps the more crucial factor is that both signs respect each other. Aquarius loves life and originality, and is quite intellectual. Libra is similar, but more balanced and rather less eccentric. A visit to this couple's house would be entertaining and full of zany wit, activity and excitement. Both are keen to travel and may prefer to 'find themselves' before taking on too many domestic responsibilities. Star rating: *****

Aquarius meets Scorpio

This is a promising and practical combination. Scorpio responds well to Aquarius' persistent exploration of its deep nature and so this generally shy sign becomes lighter, brighter and more inspirational. Meanwhile, Aquarians are rarely as sure of themselves as they like to appear and are reassured by Scorpio's constant, steady and determined support. Both signs want to be kind to each other, which is a good starting point to a relationship that should be warm most of the time and extremely hot occasionally. Star rating: ****

Aquarius meets Sagittarius

Both Sagittarius and Aquarius are into mind games, which may lead to something of an intellectual competition. If one side is happy to be 'bamboozled' it won't be a problem, but it is more likely that the relationship will turn into a competition, which won't auger well for its long-term future. However, on the plus side, both signs are adventurous and sociable, so as long as there is always something new and interesting to do, the match could turn out very well. Star rating: **

Aquarius meets Capricorn

Probably one of the least likely combinations, as Capricorn and Aquarius are unlikely to choose each other in the first place, unless one side is quite untypical of their sign. Capricorn approaches things in a practical way and likes to get things done, while Aquarius works almost exclusively for the moment and relies heavily on intuition. Their attitudes to romance are also diametrically opposed: Aquarius' moods tend to swing from red hot to ice cold in a minute, which is alien to steady Capricorn. Star rating: **

VENUS:
THE PLANET OF LOVE

If you look up at the sky around sunset or sunrise you will often see Venus in close attendance to the Sun. It is arguably one of the most beautiful sights of all and there is little wonder that historically it became associated with the goddess of love. But although Venus does play an important part in the way you view love and in the way others see you romantically, this is only one of the spheres of influence that it enjoys in your overall character.

Venus has a part to play in the more cultured side of your life and has much to do with your appreciation of art, literature, music and general creativity. Even the way you look is responsive to the part of the zodiac that Venus occupied at the start of your life, though this fact is also down to your Sun sign and Ascending sign. If, at the time you were born, Venus occupied one of the more gregarious zodiac signs, you will be more likely to wear your heart on your sleeve, as well as to be more attracted to entertainment, social gatherings and good company. If on the other hand Venus occupied a quiet zodiac sign at the time of your birth, you would tend to be more retiring and less willing to shine in public situations.

It's good to know what part the planet Venus plays in your life, for it can have a great bearing on the way you appear to the rest of the world and since we all have to mix with others, you can learn to make the very best of what Venus has to offer you.

One of the great complications in the past has always been trying to establish exactly what zodiac position Venus enjoyed when you were born, because the planet is notoriously difficult to track. However, I have solved that problem by creating a table that is exclusive to your Sun sign, which you will find on the following page.

Establishing your Venus sign could not be easier. Just look up the year of your birth on the page opposite and you will see a sign of the zodiac. This was the sign that Venus occupied in the period covered by your sign in that year. If Venus occupied more than one sign during the period, this is indicated by the date on which the sign changed, and the name of the new sign. For instance, if you were born in 1945, Venus was in Pisces until the 12th February, after which time it was in Aries. If you were born before 12th February your Venus sign is Pisces, if you were born on or after 12th February, your Venus sign is Aries. Once you have established the position of Venus at the time of your birth, you can then look in the pages which follow to see how this has a bearing on your life as a whole.

1919 AQUARIUS / 3.2 PISCES
1920 SAGITTARIUS / 30.1 CAPRICORN
1921 PISCES / 15.2 ARIES
1922 CAPRICORN / 25.1 AQUARIUS /
   18.2 PISCES
1923 SAGITTARIUS / 7.2 CAPRICORN
1924 PISCES / 13.2 ARIES
1925 CAPRICORN / 9.2 AQUARIUS
1926 AQUARIUS
1927 AQUARIUS / 2.2 PISCES
1928 SAGITTARIUS / 29.1 CAPRICORN
1929 PISCES / 14.2 ARIES
1930 CAPRICORN / 25.1 AQUARIUS /
   18.2 PISCES
1931 SAGITTARIUS / 6.2 CAPRICORN
1932 PISCES / 13.2 ARIES
1933 CAPRICORN / 8.2 AQUARIUS
1934 AQUARIUS
1935 AQUARIUS / 2.2 PISCES
1936 SAGITTARIUS / 29.1 CAPRICORN
1937 PISCES / 13.2 ARIES
1938 CAPRICORN / 24.1 AQUARIUS /
   17.2 PISCES
1939 SAGITTARIUS / 6.2 CAPRICORN
1940 PISCES / 12.2 ARIES
1941 CAPRICORN / 8.2 AQUARIUS
1942 AQUARIUS
1943 AQUARIUS / 1.2 PISCES
1944 SAGITTARIUS / 28.1 CAPRICORN
1945 PISCES / 12.2 ARIES
1946 CAPRICORN / 24.1 AQUARIUS /
   17.2 PISCES
1947 SAGITTARIUS / 6.2 CAPRICORN
1948 PISCES / 12.2 ARIES
1949 CAPRICORN / 7.2 AQUARIUS
1950 AQUARIUS
1951 AQUARIUS / 1.2 PISCES
1952 SAGITTARIUS / 27.1 CAPRICORN
1953 PISCES / 11.2 ARIES
1954 CAPRICORN / 23.1 AQUARIUS /
   16.2 PISCES
1955 SAGITTARIUS / 6.2 CAPRICORN
1956 PISCES / 11.2 ARIES
1957 CAPRICORN / 7.2 AQUARIUS
1958 AQUARIUS
1959 AQUARIUS / 31.1 PISCES
1960 SAGITTARIUS / 27.1 CAPRICORN
1961 PISCES / 9.2 ARIES
1962 CAPRICORN / 23.1 AQUARIUS /
   15.2 PISCES
1963 SAGITTARIUS / 6.2 CAPRICORN
1964 PISCES / 11.2 ARIES
1965 CAPRICORN / 6.2 AQUARIUS
1966 AQUARIUS
1967 AQUARIUS / 30.1 PISCES
1968 SAGITTARIUS / 26.1 CAPRICORN

1969 PISCES / 7.2 ARIES
1970 CAPRICORN / 22.1 AQUARIUS /
   15.2 PISCES
1971 SAGITTARIUS / 5.2 CAPRICORN
1972 PISCES / 10.2 ARIES
1973 CAPRICORN / 5.2 AQUARIUS
1974 AQUARIUS / 7.2 CAPRICORN
1975 AQUARIUS / 30.1 PISCES
1976 SAGITTARIUS / 26.1 CAPRICORN
1977 PISCES / 5.2 ARIES
1978 CAPRICORN / 22.1 AQUARIUS /
   14.2 PISCES
1979 SAGITTARIUS / 5.2 CAPRICORN
1980 PISCES / 10.2 ARIES
1981 CAPRICORN / 5.2 AQUARIUS
1982 AQUARIUS / 29.1 CAPRICORN
1983 AQUARIUS / 29.1 PISCES
1984 SAGITTARIUS / 25.1 CAPRICORN
1985 PISCES / 5.2 ARIES
1986 AQUARIUS / 14.2 PISCES
1987 SAGITTARIUS / 5.2 CAPRICORN
1988 PISCES / 9.2 ARIES
1989 CAPRICORN / 4.2 AQUARIUS
1990 AQUARIUS / 23.1 CAPRICORN
1991 AQUARIUS / 29.1 PISCES
1992 SAGITTARIUS / 25.1 CAPRICORN
1993 PISCES / 4.2 ARIES
1994 AQUARIUS / 13.2 PISCES
1995 SAGITTARIUS / 5.2 CAPRICORN
1996 PISCES / 9.2 ARIES
1997 CAPRICORN / 4.2 AQUARIUS
1998 AQUARIUS / 23.1 CAPRICORN
1999 AQUARIUS / 29.1 PISCES
2000 SAGITTARIUS / 25.1 CAPRICORN
2001 PISCES / 4.2 ARIES
2002 AQUARIUS / 13.2 PISCES
2003 SAGITTARIUS
2004 PISCES / 9.2 AQUARIUS
2005 CAPRICORN / 6.2 AQUARIUS
2006 AQUARIUS / 14.1 CAPRICORN
2007 AQUARIUS / 29.1 PISCES
2008 SAGITTARIUS / 25.1 CAPRICORN
2009 PISCES / 4.2 ARIES
2010 AQUARIUS / 12.2 PISCES
2011 SAGITTARIUS
2012 PISCES / 9.2 AQUARIUS
2013 CAPRICORN / 6.2 AQUARIUS
2014 CAPRICORN / 6.2 AQUARIUS
2015 AQUARIUS / 29.1 PISCES
2016 SAGITTARIUS / 24.1 AQUARIUS
2017 PISCES / 4.2 ARIES

VENUS THROUGH THE ZODIAC SIGNS

Venus in Aries

Amongst other things, the position of Venus in Aries indicates a fondness for travel, music and all creative pursuits. Your nature tends to be affectionate and you would try not to create confusion or difficulty for others if it could be avoided. Many people with this planetary position have a great love of the theatre, and mental stimulation is of the greatest importance. Early romantic attachments are common with Venus in Aries, so it is very important to establish a genuine sense of romantic continuity. Early marriage is not recommended, especially if it is based on sympathy. You may give your heart a little too readily on occasions.

Venus in Taurus

You are capable of very deep feelings and your emotions tend to last for a very long time. This makes you a trusting partner and lover, whose constancy is second to none. In life you are precise and careful and always try to do things the right way. Although this means an ordered life, which you are comfortable with, it can also lead you to be rather too fussy for your own good. Despite your pleasant nature, you are very fixed in your opinions and quite able to speak your mind. Others are attracted to you and historical astrologers always quoted this position of Venus as being very fortunate in terms of marriage. However, if you find yourself involved in a failed relationship, it could take you a long time to trust again.

Venus in Gemini

As with all associations related to Gemini, you tend to be quite versatile, anxious for change and intelligent in your dealings with the world at large. You may gain money from more than one source but you are equally good at spending it. There is an inference here that you are a good communicator, via either the written or the spoken word, and you love to be in the company of interesting people. Always on the look-out for culture, you may also be very fond of music, and love to indulge the curious and cultured side of your nature. In romance you tend to have more than one relationship and could find yourself associated with someone who has previously been a friend or even a distant relative.

Venus in Cancer

You often stay close to home because you are very fond of family and enjoy many of your most treasured moments when you are with those you love. Being naturally sympathetic, you will always do anything you can to support those around you, even people you hardly know at all. This charitable side of your nature is your most noticeable trait and is one of the reasons why others are naturally so fond of you. Being receptive and in some cases even psychic, you can see through to the soul of most of those with whom you come into contact. You may not commence too many romantic attachments but when you do give your heart, it tends to be unconditionally.

Venus in Leo

It must become quickly obvious to almost anyone you meet that you are kind, sympathetic and yet determined enough to stand up for anyone or anything that is truly important to you. Bright and sunny, you warm the world with your natural enthusiasm and would rarely do anything to hurt those around you, or at least not intentionally. In romance you are ardent and sincere, though some may find your style just a little overpowering. Gains come through your contacts with other people and this could be especially true with regard to romance, for love and money often come hand in hand for those who were born with Venus in Leo. People claim to understand you, though you are more complex than you seem.

Venus in Virgo

Your nature could well be fairly quiet no matter what your Sun sign might be, though this fact often manifests itself as an inner peace and would not prevent you from being basically sociable. Some delays and even the odd disappointment in love cannot be ruled out with this planetary position, though it's a fact that you will usually find the happiness you look for in the end. Catapulting yourself into romantic entanglements that you know to be rather ill-advised is not sensible, and it would be better to wait before you committed yourself exclusively to any one person. It is the essence of your nature to serve the world at large and through doing so it is possible that you will attract money at some stage in your life.

Venus in Libra

Venus is very comfortable in Libra and bestows upon those people who have this planetary position a particular sort of kindness that is easy to recognise. This is a very good position for all sorts of friendships and also for romantic attachments that usually bring much joy into your life. Few individuals with Venus in Libra would avoid marriage and since you are capable of great depths of love, it is likely that you will find a contented personal life. You like to mix with people of integrity and intelligence but don't take kindly to scruffy surroundings or work that means getting your hands too dirty. Careful speculation, good business dealings and money through marriage all seem fairly likely.

Venus in Scorpio

You are quite open and tend to spend money quite freely, even on those occasions when you don't have very much. Although your intentions are always good, there are times when you get yourself in to the odd scrape and this can be particularly true when it comes to romance, which you may come to late or from a rather unexpected direction. Certainly you have the power to be happy and to make others contented on the way, but you find the odd stumbling block on your journey through life and it could seem that you have to work harder than those around you. As a result of this, you gain a much deeper understanding of the true value of personal happiness than many people ever do, and are likely to achieve true contentment in the end.

Venus in Sagittarius

You are lighthearted, cheerful and always able to see the funny side of any situation. These facts enhance your popularity, which is especially high with members of the opposite sex. You should never have to look too far to find romantic interest in your life, though it is just possible that you might be too willing to commit yourself before you are certain that the person in question is right for you. Part of the problem here extends to other areas of life too. The fact is that you like variety in everything and so can tire of situations that fail to offer it. All the same, if you choose wisely and learn to understand your restless side, then great happiness can be yours.

Venus in Capricorn

The most notable trait that comes from Venus in this position is that it makes you trustworthy and able to take on all sorts of responsibilities in life. People are instinctively fond of you and love you all the more because you are always ready to help those who are in any form of need. Social and business popularity can be yours and there is a magnetic quality to your nature that is particularly attractive in a romantic sense. Anyone who wants a partner for a lover, a spouse and a good friend too would almost certainly look in your direction. Constancy is the hallmark of your nature and unfaithfulness would go right against the grain. You might sometimes be a little too trusting.

Venus in Aquarius

This location of Venus offers a fondness for travel and a desire to try out something new at every possible opportunity. You are extremely easy to get along with and tend to have many friends from varied backgrounds, classes and inclinations. You like to live a distinct sort of life and gain a great deal from moving about, both in a career sense and with regard to your home. It is not out of the question that you could form a romantic attachment to someone who comes from far away or be attracted to a person of a distinctly artistic and original nature. What you cannot stand is jealousy, for you have friends of both sexes and would want to keep things that way.

Venus in Pisces

The first thing people tend to notice about you is your wonderful, warm smile. Being very charitable by nature you will do anything to help others, even if you don't know them well. Much of your life may be spent sorting out situations for other people, but it is very important to feel that you are living for yourself too. In the main, you remain cheerful, and tend to be quite attractive to members of the opposite sex. Where romantic attachments are concerned, you could be drawn to people who are significantly older or younger than yourself or to someone with a unique career or point of view. It might be best for you to avoid marrying whilst you are still very young.

HOW THE DIAGRAMS WORK

Through the picture diagrams in the Astral Diary I want to help you to plot your year. With them you can see where the positive and negative aspects will be found in each month. To make the most of them, all you have to do is remember where and when!

Let me show you how they work ...

THE MONTH AT A GLANCE

Just as there are twelve separate zodiac signs, so astrologers believe that each sign has twelve separate aspects to life. Each of the twelve segments relates to a different personal aspect. I list them all every month so that their meanings are always clear.

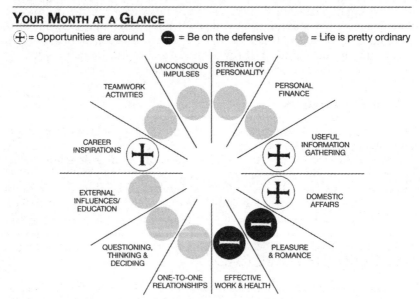

YOUR MONTH AT A GLANCE

$\oplus$ = Opportunities are around   ⊖ = Be on the defensive   ● = Life is pretty ordinary

- UNCONSCIOUS IMPULSES
- STRENGTH OF PERSONALITY
- TEAMWORK ACTIVITIES
- PERSONAL FINANCE
- CAREER INSPIRATIONS
- USEFUL INFORMATION GATHERING
- EXTERNAL INFLUENCES/ EDUCATION
- DOMESTIC AFFAIRS
- QUESTIONING, THINKING & DECIDING
- PLEASURE & ROMANCE
- ONE-TO-ONE RELATIONSHIPS
- EFFECTIVE WORK & HEALTH

I have designed this chart to show you how and when these twelve different aspects are being influenced throughout the year. When there is a shaded circle, nothing out of the ordinary is to be expected. However, when a circle turns white with a plus sign, the influence is positive. Where the circle is black with a minus sign, it is a negative.

YOUR ENERGY RHYTHM CHART

Below is a picture diagram in which I link your zodiac group to the rhythm of the Moon. In doing this I have calculated when you will be gaining strength from its influence and equally when you may be weakened by it.

If you think of yourself as being like the tides of the ocean then you may understand how your own energies must also rise and fall. And if you understand how it works and when it is working, then you can better organise your activities to achieve more and get things done more easily.

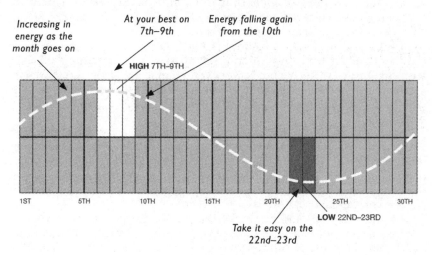

THE KEY DAYS

Some of the entries are in **bold**, which indicates the working of astrological cycles in your life. Look out for them each week as they are the best days to take action or make decisions. The daily text tells you which area of your life to focus on.

MERCURY RETROGRADE

The Mercury symbol (☿) indicates that Mercury is retrograde on that day. Since Mercury governs communication, the fact that it appears to be moving backwards when viewed from the Earth at this time should warn you that your communication skills are not likely to be at their best and you could expect some setbacks.

AQUARIUS: YOUR YEAR IN BRIEF

It should be fairly certain this year that you know what you want and how you should go about getting it. January offers incentives, even if the winter weather gets you down. Trends look favourable for success during the colder months this year and so it would be worth putting in extra effort right at the start of the year, which will pay handsome dividends later. Expect changes to your work and, if possible, embrace them.

It is likely that March and April will find you waking up to the reality of the seasons and getting on with domestic matters in an especially productive way. The possibility of changes at work continues, particularly during March, and there may also be the promise of new romantic interest for some. General good luck starts to improve and you are once again benefitting as a result of past efforts.

As the year moves on, May and June are likely to find you travelling. After a generally stay-at-home period at the very start of May, you will waken to the unavoidable call of new places and faces. With plenty to play for in the professional stakes, this could be turn out to be an important year in terms of your career. Not everyone will be on your side at this time but when it matters you can find supporters.

July and August could be the busiest part of the year as far as you are concerned and they indicate a spirit of compromise, as well as the chance to look in new directions. At work you are likely to be very busy and constantly in demand, whilst retired Aquarians or those between jobs could be discovering newer and interesting ways in which to fill their time. Action is forecast when it comes to travel and one or two of your journeys could come free of charge.

It is extremely unlikely that you will get everything you want during September and October but you could come close. This is a time when all the effort you put in earlier in the year begins to pay dividends. People you don't see often may return to your life and you are once again thinking seriously about what long-term relationships have to offer you. Confidence grows and a more mature Aquarian begins to show as the year draws towards its close.

In a confident mood during November and December you may be able to realise some of your earlier ambitions and although, in spite of your birth sign, this may not be the time of year you relish the most, you bring your own sunshine into the world because of your attitude. Christmas could be noteworthy for its surprises, perhaps in the family if not for you directly.

2017

Your Month at a Glance

⊕ = Opportunities are around   ⊖ = Be on the defensive   ⬤ = Life is pretty ordinary

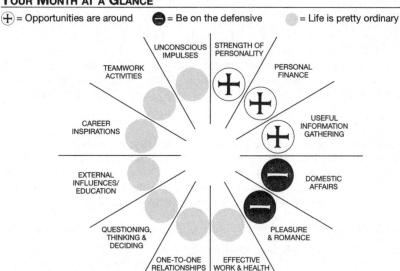

January Highs and Lows

Here I show you how the rhythms of the Moon will affect you this month. Like the tide, your energies and abilities will rise and fall with its pattern. When it is above the centre line, go for it, when it is below, you should be resting.

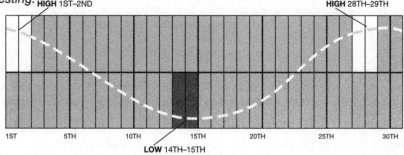

45

1 SUNDAY ☿ *Moon Age Day 4   Moon Sign Aquarius*

The first day of January should find you in a good mood and ready to have a go at almost anything. The ambitious qualities within your nature are presently very strong, leading to a willingness to take a chance. Your year has begun with the monthly lunar high, when the Moon is in your own zodiac sign, and that means general good luck could be paying you a visit.

2 MONDAY ☿ *Moon Age Day 5   Moon Sign Aquarius*

Risky ventures are par for the course because you are extremely adventurous and quite physical in your approach to life right now. Almost any opportunity that comes along is grist to the mill of both your curiosity and your determination. With good social skills and a disarming manner, you should be at the top of the popularity stakes.

3 TUESDAY ☿ *Moon Age Day 6   Moon Sign Pisces*

In a social sense you have particularly winning ways now and can get most of what you want from other people. Turn on the charm and see how easily people come around to your very reasonable point of view. Although the weather outside might not be very good at present, you shouldn't mind this and a little fresh air would do you no harm at all.

4 WEDNESDAY ☿ *Moon Age Day 7   Moon Sign Pisces*

Social developments continue unabated and you could find some attention coming your way from a most unexpected direction. Keep a sense of proportion when dealing with younger family members or friends who seem determined to throw a spanner in the works. Avoid arguments at all costs today.

5 THURSDAY ☿ *Moon Age Day 8   Moon Sign Aries*

Although you may encounter a little resistance from certain quarters, in the main you are progressive and positive, which makes those around you sit up and take notice. Conforming to expected patterns of behaviour could prove to be far easier than you might have expected and you can make a big splash socially.

6 FRIDAY ☿ *Moon Age Day 9   Moon Sign Aries*

Look out for romance today because it isn't very far from you at the moment. Just being yourself is enough to attract attention from some quite unexpected directions and you can turn heads at every street corner. In more practical matters, keep a sense of proportion with regard to new schemes, and be prepared to accept that some of them may not be realistic.

7 SATURDAY   ☿   *Moon Age Day 10   Moon Sign Taurus*

You will certainly have your work cut out when it comes to dealing with material demands right now. You might struggle to get your priorities right and you will need to be especially delicate when you stand on the sensibilities of other people. Go out of your way to handle matters as tactfully as possible.

8 SUNDAY   *Moon Age Day 11   Moon Sign Taurus*

Your sympathies are easily stirred today, probably because your heart goes out to people who you know are not as fortunate as you are. Don't allow yourself to become weighed down with responsibilities that aren't yours, though of course it's important to lend a hand when you can if others are in need of it.

9 MONDAY   *Moon Age Day 12   Moon Sign Gemini*

Your personal impact on others is very strong indeed. Keep abreast of things that are happening in and around your home at the moment because you can clearly benefit from some of them. Planetary trends indicate that friends should be especially helpful right now and may have important news to impart, so keep your ears open.

10 TUESDAY   *Moon Age Day 13   Moon Sign Gemini*

This is not a time to allow yourself to become bored with routines or conventions for which you can see point whatsoever. It's clear that there is plenty of work to be done so put these thoughts aside and get cracking as early in the day as you can manage. It may not be easy to find time to call your own today.

11 WEDNESDAY   *Moon Age Day 14   Moon Sign Cancer*

Personal dealings with others are a focus for some of your attention at present. Trends suggest that this will be a social day, and a time when you find it easy to give your attention to matters that are not in the least practical. Don't worry about this – everyone has to have fun sometimes and this ought to be such a period for you.

12 THURSDAY   *Moon Age Day 15   Moon Sign Cancer*

So long as you don't take yourself, or anyone else for that matter, too much for granted all should go reasonably well at this time. It appears that you are in the mood to compromise on important matters, which will please colleagues and friends. At home, there are words of affection coming your way before long.

13 FRIDAY

Moon Age Day 16   Moon Sign Cancer

Strong and idealistic at the moment, you won't settle for anything less than what you know to be fair and just. That's fine but it won't help if you cut off your nose to spite your face. There are many ways of going about doing things, a fact that you need to bear in mind before you open your mouth too much right now.

14 SATURDAY

Moon Age Day 17   Moon Sign Leo

The monthly lunar low comes around, a lull patch which isn't something you can do a great deal about. Settle for a stay at home sort of Saturday if you can, and be willing to address family concerns if needed. Preparing yourself for something that lies ahead is important, and you may find that a little gentle activity isn't the ordeal you are expecting.

15 SUNDAY

Moon Age Day 18   Moon Sign Leo

Attend to any unfinished business as soon as you can. This is not the time to keep either people or situations waiting. Once you know you are on top of things then you can spend time enjoying yourself, but trends suggest that this probably won't be for at least the first part of what is likely to be a somewhat dull day.

16 MONDAY

Moon Age Day 19   Moon Sign Virgo

You certainly have the gift of the gab today and won't fight shy of saying what you think. The true originality of your zodiac sign is on display and you feel fairly confident with most of your decisions. If situations arise in which you feel you don't know what you are doing you should be willing to seek help.

17 TUESDAY

Moon Age Day 20   Moon Sign Virgo

Even if others tend to keep you waiting you will plough ahead, doing your own thing and making it plain that you won't be held up by anything or anyone. When you can't get a positive reaction, you tend to talk your way through situations, something you are especially good at doing under present planetary trends.

18 WEDNESDAY

Moon Age Day 21   Moon Sign Libra

Be bold and brave when dealing with bullies, no matter what sphere of your life in which they show up. The more off-the-wall qualities of Aquarius are now on display and not everyone will be able to understand what makes you tick. Even if you are presently faced with a mountain of work, you will deal with it efficiently.

19 THURSDAY
Moon Age Day 22   Moon Sign Libra

Relatives and friends may have it in their minds to mess you about today but you are not about to allow that to happen. Your intuition is razor sharp now and there isn't much doubt that you are equal to just about anyone's tricks. What you have in great abundance right now is a strong sense of humour, so put this to good use.

20 FRIDAY
Moon Age Day 23   Moon Sign Scorpio

This Friday offers you the chance to stand fairly and squarely in the limelight. The only real requirement is that you understand fully what is being expected of you. Should you be unsure about anything, make certain you get on top of the situation before you are put to the test in a very public way. Aquarius is never comfortable when out of its depth.

21 SATURDAY
Moon Age Day 24   Moon Sign Scorpio

Explore a new possibility, perhaps one that means some sort of business partnership. You might not be able to do much about this on a Saturday but you can at least put plans into action and talk to the right people. Congratulations might be in order somewhere within the family and you won't be tardy in offering them.

22 SUNDAY
Moon Age Day 25   Moon Sign Scorpio

Confidence is all you need to keep pushing on. Direct progress might be somewhat difficult on a Sunday and you might have to settle instead for some advance planning. Your determination to move forward occupies most of your thoughts, though you do need to take some time out to simply enjoy yourself, possibly in the company of your partner.

23 MONDAY
Moon Age Day 26   Moon Sign Sagittarius

Start new projects as you mean to go on, especially those associated with house and home. You may find that people will gang together to help you at the moment and so this is a good time to get things done. Your capacity for keeping going is good but today might have less sparkle in the social and romantic departments.

24 TUESDAY
Moon Age Day 27   Moon Sign Sagittarius

You cannot afford to give anyone the impression you will waver today. The adage 'give an inch and people will take a mile' seems to be very appropriate. Present trends indicate that it will be necessary to stick to your original views in a number of matters. Even if this means you are stubborn, at least people will toe the line.

25 WEDNESDAY *Moon Age Day 28   Moon Sign Capricorn*

There is plenty to be done today, though you are able to commit yourself to whatever is at hand and happy to work on steadily. Even though this is the midweek period you also need to spend at least some time relaxing. Out of preference you will probably mix freely with friends you find to be particularly amusing.

26 THURSDAY *Moon Age Day 29   Moon Sign Capricorn*

Keep a sense of proportion regarding situations that seem to be running out of control. This is not a time to panic about anything, nothing will be gained that way and instead you can do yourself a great deal of good by simply playing it cool. If it is fame or even notoriety you are after, this could be just the time you are looking for.

27 FRIDAY *Moon Age Day 0   Moon Sign Capricorn*

With a strong sense of purpose, but perhaps not too much confidence, you begin something new at this time. You can be sure of support, particularly from colleagues and friends. The fact that the Moon is presently in your solar twelfth house won't be too much help but you are likely to manage somehow.

28 SATURDAY *Moon Age Day 1   Moon Sign Aquarius*

Your personality is now enticing and exciting, making it easy for you to attract converts to just about any cause you decide to follow. In particular, trends suggest that you might experience a little general good luck and can perhaps afford some measured and well thought out speculation. This would be an ideal time for travel for most Aquarian people.

29 SUNDAY *Moon Age Day 2   Moon Sign Aquarius*

You are still putting on a very positive face to the world and won't want to let up when you know you are getting close to a number of important objectives. Although you won't find it too easy to persuade everyone you know what you are talking about, a dose of your sense of humour should swing it for you.

30 MONDAY *Moon Age Day 3   Moon Sign Pisces*

A careful appraisal of romantic attachments tells you that matters of love are bang on course. In addition, you enjoy a high degree of popularity at this time and can be certain to get the sort of support you would wish. Plan now for next weekend and also for business ventures that are about to commence.

31 TUESDAY
Moon Age Day 4   Moon Sign Pisces

Trends suggest that there may be some unusual situations to deal with today and you might feel that your mind is somewhat more muddled than has been the case of late. It is possible that you are somehow out of your depth may find it difficult to break through the entrenched ideas that others are displaying at present.

2017

YOUR MONTH AT A GLANCE

⊕ = Opportunities are around   ⊖ = Be on the defensive   ● = Life is pretty ordinary

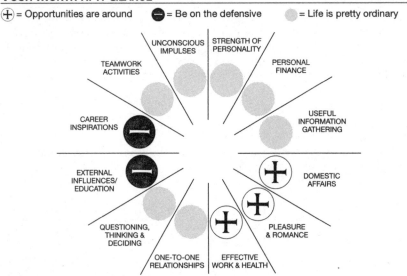

UNCONSCIOUS IMPULSES
STRENGTH OF PERSONALITY
TEAMWORK ACTIVITIES
PERSONAL FINANCE
CAREER INSPIRATIONS
USEFUL INFORMATION GATHERING
EXTERNAL INFLUENCES/ EDUCATION
DOMESTIC AFFAIRS
QUESTIONING, THINKING & DECIDING
PLEASURE & ROMANCE
ONE-TO-ONE RELATIONSHIPS
EFFECTIVE WORK & HEALTH

FEBRUARY HIGHS AND LOWS

Here I show you how the rhythms of the Moon will affect you this month. Like the tide, your energies and abilities will rise and fall with its pattern. When it is above the centre line, go for it, when it is below, you should be resting.

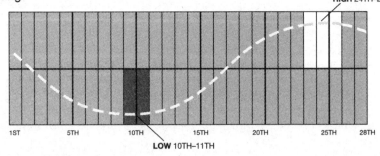

HIGH 24TH–26TH

1ST   5TH   10TH   15TH   20TH   25TH   28TH

LOW 10TH–11TH

I WEDNESDAY
Moon Age Day 5   Moon Sign Aries

Getting to grips with certain facts and figures will take up a percentage of your day, which is why there might not be all that much time for relaxation today. It is possible that practical matters will be on your mind a great deal and that you may also be planning some significant changes in and around your home.

2 THURSDAY
Moon Age Day 6   Moon Sign Aries

Life can have its emotional downside, which is why you need to get any personal disputes out of the way as soon as possible. This is not a day during which you should dwell on things or take matters out of context. In all probability your level of sensitivity is a little too high right now and things may not be as bad as they appear to you.

3 FRIDAY
Moon Age Day 7   Moon Sign Aries

You now become more competitive in your dealings with the world in general. Being especially creative at the moment, you might want to take on projects that prove your artistic flair, even if you don't think you have one. If you experience some confusion over details at work, these can be easily resolved if you talk things through.

4 SATURDAY
Moon Age Day 8   Moon Sign Taurus

Relationships are inclined to try your patience today and might even seem as though they are more trouble than they are worth. Put aside any tendency to avoid serious issues and instead do what you can to be both determined and bold when it counts the most. It's important for others to know exactly how you feel.

5 SUNDAY
Moon Age Day 9   Moon Sign Taurus

When it comes to making an impact on others this seems to be the month for Aquarius. There are a few astrological reasons why this is the case, not least of all the present position of the Sun in your solar first house. Get out and make the most of it – showing people what makes you tick should be the easiest task of all.

6 MONDAY
Moon Age Day 10   Moon Sign Gemini

Keep sight of practical necessities and don't allow yourself to be browbeaten into situations that are not of your own personal choosing. You could do with some space today, in order to think things through, but the fact is that you are unlikely to get it. All in all you are probably proving to be more successful than you think.

7 TUESDAY
Moon Age Day 11   Moon Sign Gemini

It shouldn't be too difficult for you to make compromises if they are required right now and this will lead to better relationships all round. This ought to be a reasonably comfortable sort of day, even if it doesn't turn out to be an especially successful one. A problem can be shelved or passed sideways to another individual.

8 WEDNESDAY
Moon Age Day 12   Moon Sign Cancer

In intimate relationships you could notice now that certain sacrifices have to be made. This isn't too difficult for you but it might mean having to eat some humble pie because of the way you have dealt with things in the past. Trends suggest that some good news could come your way, certainly before next weekend.

9 THURSDAY
Moon Age Day 13   Moon Sign Cancer

The planets in your chart now tell us that much of life is currently geared towards feelings of personal security. There may seem to be some intrigue around, possibly coming from the direction of people you know quite well – or at least thought you did. Certain commitments at this time just cannot be avoided.

10 FRIDAY
Moon Age Day 14   Moon Sign Leo

Working towards moderate expectations is a good idea today, as would be keeping specific ideas to yourself. There is a great danger that you could give someone a sniff at plans you are laying down and thereby lose your edge. Casual conversation is fine, as is finding ways to please family members.

11 SATURDAY
Moon Age Day 15   Moon Sign Leo

Making genuine progress isn't easy while the Moon is in Leo, your opposite zodiac sign. The lunar low isn't particularly potent this time around but you might find that both relatives and friends seem rather uncommitted today. The fault is no doubt yours but you can't see why for the moment.

12 SUNDAY
Moon Age Day 16   Moon Sign Virgo

You are certainly more assertive in arguments right now and won't take no for an answer when you are determined to get a yes. Few people can stand up to you when you are in this frame of mind, and only the odd brave soul would try to do so. Be careful you don't come across as being too pushy or you risk alienating others.

13 MONDAY
Moon Age Day 17   Moon Sign Virgo

The continued planetary focus is on work and a sense of personal security, which is quite important to you at this time. Avoid giving the wrong impression, especially to your partner, by being willing to explain your point of view fully. It is possible that in conversation you may come across as rather more adamant than you feel.

14 TUESDAY
Moon Age Day 18   Moon Sign Libra

Your personality is very much to the fore today and you are giving a good account of yourself in all social situations. Not everyone will be on your side at present but the people who matter the most should prove to be very supportive. Today might not be extraordinary but it can be quite useful

15 WEDNESDAY
Moon Age Day 19   Moon Sign Libra

Being in the limelight will probably appeal to you a great deal now. That isn't too surprising because you are born under an Air sign, and all the Air signs enjoy a degree of popularity. Getting your own way in social situations should be both easy and fun. Practically, anything you turn your hand to now is likely to work out well.

16 THURSDAY
Moon Age Day 20   Moon Sign Libra

You might be looking at people you don't know very well today and finding yourself relying heavily on them. Use your intuition, which won't let you down. If you know instinctively that someone is worthy of your trust, then this is likely to be the case. This would be a good day to get out and about and perhaps do some shopping.

17 FRIDAY
Moon Age Day 21   Moon Sign Scorpio

People are simply not reliable now, which is why you are doing most things for yourself. You may have to reorder your schedule somewhat today, so as to leave time for possibilities that are only now coming into your mind. Most of the time you will be reacting to what is going on around you rather than devising the plans.

18 SATURDAY
Moon Age Day 22   Moon Sign Scorpio

Appointments may have to be altered at short notice and you will certainly have to get used to interruptions because they come along all the time today. Happily, these are only minor inconveniences to spoil what should be an otherwise steady and positive sort of day. You are gradually growing more competitive.

19 SUNDAY
Moon Age Day 23   Moon Sign Sagittarius

There are people around today who can prove to be very helpful – most likely individuals who are experts in their own particular field. You won't be tardy when it comes to seeking out such types. Socially speaking, you seem to be on great form and will move heaven and earth to make this a fun Sunday.

20 MONDAY
Moon Age Day 24   Moon Sign Sagittarius

You are very reactive today, which is why if you spend too much time doing only what is expected of you, boredom is likely to follow. Variety is certainly the spice of your life this week and you will become unsettled if it isn't present. Aquarius is on the move, even if you don't know where you are going yet.

21 TUESDAY
Moon Age Day 25   Moon Sign Sagittarius

This could be a family-motivated period for many Aquarians. The weather outside may not be very inspiring which could lead to the comfy desire to stay at home and put your feet up. Luckily, although there are tasks you have to perform, most of them can be out of the way quickly, leaving you time for the relaxation you crave.

22 WEDNESDAY
Moon Age Day 26   Moon Sign Capricorn

Much of what happens today is left up to your own imagination. With a fairly neutral day in store, yet plenty of ability to have a bearing on circumstances, it appears that you are showing a very inventive side to your nature. Today might not be exactly exciting but it can prove to be eventful – the choice is up to you.

23 THURSDAY
Moon Age Day 27   Moon Sign Capricorn

Expect a more reactive sort of day and be willing to take the decisions necessary in order to get ahead generally. A continued reliance on specific people might appear to be something of a problem, particularly if the individuals concerned are turning awkward for some reason. Take a step back and look at situations afresh.

24 FRIDAY
Moon Age Day 28   Moon Sign Aquarius

The lunar high could take you somewhat by surprise this time around, but it brings good things into every arena. Energy is present, as is your sense of humour. Being in the right place to have a significant bearing on situations is now easy and you won't find it at all difficult to back your hunches. Romance may also be looking good by the evening.

25 SATURDAY
Moon Age Day 0   Moon Sign Aquarius

You are especially tolerant of the way your relatives and friends are behaving at the moment and you won't take offhand remarks as anything more significant than they really are. With a smooth and easy view of life generally, it looks as though you can make some significant gains without having to try very hard.

26 SUNDAY
Moon Age Day 1   Moon Sign Aquarius

Unsurprisingly you now find that you are ahead of yourself, especially in terms of work. This might mean taking some time out to please yourself, though it is equally likely that you will stretch yourself towards completely new horizons. There should be an increase in your perceived popularity and better social prospects.

27 MONDAY
Moon Age Day 2   Moon Sign Pisces

Entrenched attitudes are hardly what is expected of Aquarius, so avoid them as much as you can. You get the very best of today by being amenable to change and by being willing to listen to an alternative point of view. Although you might not gain much today in a material sense you can enjoy some social highlights.

28 TUESDAY
Moon Age Day 3   Moon Sign Pisces

Whatever the weather is doing now, you would find it beneficial to get out into the fresh air. Staying cooped up all the time is no good for Aquarius and you can gain a whole new perspective standing on a windy hill or by the sea. Trends suggest that the days ahead could bring some positive challenges so for now relax.

March

2017

Your Month at a Glance

⊕ = Opportunities are around   ⊖ = Be on the defensive   ● = Life is pretty ordinary

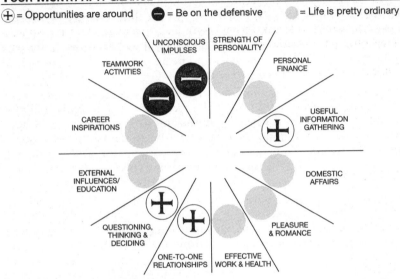

- UNCONSCIOUS IMPULSES
- STRENGTH OF PERSONALITY
- TEAMWORK ACTIVITIES
- PERSONAL FINANCE
- CAREER INSPIRATIONS
- USEFUL INFORMATION GATHERING
- EXTERNAL INFLUENCES/ EDUCATION
- DOMESTIC AFFAIRS
- QUESTIONING, THINKING & DECIDING
- PLEASURE & ROMANCE
- ONE-TO-ONE RELATIONSHIPS
- EFFECTIVE WORK & HEALTH

March Highs and Lows

Here I show you how the rhythms of the Moon will affect you this month. Like the tide, your energies and abilities will rise and fall with its pattern. When it is above the centre line, go for it, when it is below, you should be resting.

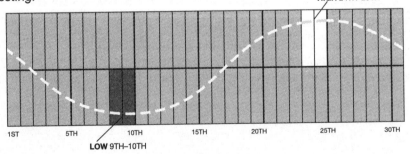

HIGH 24TH–25TH

1ST   5TH   10TH   15TH   20TH   25TH   30TH

LOW 9TH–10TH

1 WEDNESDAY *Moon Age Day 4   Moon Sign Aries*

Hoping for the best may be your attitude at the moment but that might not be quite good enough. A little extra effort could be required, especially in social situations. Plan ahead of yourself and do what you can to allay some doubts that others might have. Certain people could prove unreliable.

2 THURSDAY *Moon Age Day 5   Moon Sign Aries*

This may be the height of a rather hectic phase and one that requires extra effort from you in order to get the best from all that is happening around you. A certain restless streak comes along and you might find it distinctly advantageous to do something different, especially towards the close of the day.

3 FRIDAY *Moon Age Day 6   Moon Sign Taurus*

Try to make this a special day for yourself and your nearest and dearest. Plan a treat or simply spend more time with loved ones. The rewards could be great and you will at least have the satisfaction of knowing that you have helped someone else through their day. Try to meet up with friends if you get the chance later.

4 SATURDAY *Moon Age Day 7   Moon Sign Taurus*

Your fun loving side is definitely fully on show today. The start of the weekend offers a fun time with jokes aplenty, particularly if you allow your natural sense of humour to work overtime. Any aches and pains you experience right now are likely to be in your sides – from laughing so much!

5 SUNDAY *Moon Age Day 8   Moon Sign Gemini*

You need to feel as useful as possible now and should be looking towards completing a task that has been outstanding in your life for some time. Once you have done this, you will have more time to please yourself, and maybe to begin some sort of project that you have been dreaming about for many months.

6 MONDAY *Moon Age Day 9   Moon Sign Gemini*

Along comes a time of genuine romantic promise. You can find exactly the right words to say 'I love you' even if your partner is not in a particularly receptive mood. Your natural curiosity also comes into play now and finds you investigating situations and ideas that take your interest now.

7 TUESDAY
Moon Age Day 10   Moon Sign Cancer

Try to get as much variety into your life as you can manage. Allowing yourself to become stuck in any sort of rut would certainly be a mistake. The fact is that Aquarius needs a great deal of stimulation, most of which comes from your intellectual knockabouts with likeminded people. Enjoy these encounters and the chance to exercise your brainpower.

8 WEDNESDAY
Moon Age Day 11   Moon Sign Cancer

Trends now indicate that unexpected obligations will come along and there isn't much you can do except respond to them in the best way you can. If you feel particularly tired today there is no shame in deciding to take a short break. You will feel all the better for it and should function far more efficiently as a result.

9 THURSDAY
Moon Age Day 12   Moon Sign Leo

A certain item on today's agenda probably won't work out in quite the way you had been expecting. Never mind, review the situation and, if you need to, start again. You have great patience at the moment and it doesn't really matter how many times you have to recommence. All that matters is your final success.

10 FRIDAY
Moon Age Day 13   Moon Sign Leo

This is a day for keeping a low profile. The Moon is in your opposite sign and doing you no real favours. What might prove pleasant would be to spend some relaxation time with friends or family members. In this way you can allow the lunar low to pass almost unnoticed – but make sure that you are not expected to run any show single-handed.

11 SATURDAY
Moon Age Day 14   Moon Sign Virgo

Don't turn a blind eye to certain details that you know you will have to attend to sooner or later. It would be far better to get them behind you as soon as possible, leaving more time for enjoyment later in the day. You'll be amazed at how much work you can actually get through at this time, and with such efficiency.

12 SUNDAY
Moon Age Day 15   Moon Sign Virgo

You may discover that attracting the good things in life is a piece of cake this Sunday, but even cake can be sickening after a while. Trends suggest that Aquarians will be deliberately seeking a little solitude today. There is a possibility that you will tolerate the people you know and love, but it looks very likely that strangers will be out for today.

13 MONDAY
Moon Age Day 16   Moon Sign Virgo

A fairly hectic phase comes along and one that requires all the attention you can muster. One possible consequence is fatigue. You don't suffer too much with tiredness as a rule but even you do have your limits. You might decide to settle for an early night, or a relaxing couple of hours chatting with friends.

14 TUESDAY
Moon Age Day 17   Moon Sign Libra

Today you will probably prefer to stay at home and to let others come to you. The social impulses inherent in your zodiac sign are present although you simply won't want to carry them around to other places, but rather enjoy them in the comfort of your home. Family members can be amusing and might have some very interesting tales to tell at this time.

15 WEDNESDAY
Moon Age Day 18   Moon Sign Libra

Once again, family matters are uppermost in your mind and it appears that you might spend more time than usual with the people you know and love the most. Of course you won't exclude friends, or even acquaintances. However, when it comes to putting in the real effort, the closer you are to someone, the greater your commitment to them.

16 THURSDAY
Moon Age Day 19   Moon Sign Scorpio

There is the possibility of some advancement today, though it tends to be of the slow and steady sort and certainly won't be quick enough to please you. It might be sensible to vary your routines as much as possible, in order to avoid the sort of boredom that can sometimes come upon you.

17 FRIDAY
Moon Age Day 20   Moon Sign Scorpio

Keeping ahead of the crowd seems to be particularly important to you right now, which is why the end of the working week is hardly likely to be a time of rest and relaxation. If there isn't anything to be done regarding present efforts, you are likely to invent a whole new raft of ideas, intentions and adventures.

18 SATURDAY
Moon Age Day 21   Moon Sign Scorpio

If other people are not fulfilling their obligations, the result is going to reflect on you. That is why you find yourself turning into something of a nag right now. Although there may be complaints, you are not arguing or urging for the sake of doing so. If you do have a go at someone, try not to feel too bad about the situation.

19 SUNDAY
Moon Age Day 22   Moon Sign Sagittarius

It looks as though you will be able to manage a dozen different jobs at the same time today and still come out on top. Don't expect help to be pouring in from every direction. There are people around at the moment who simply do not want to be a part of your dreams and schemes. There isn't much point in arguing about this – just accept it.

20 MONDAY
Moon Age Day 23   Moon Sign Sagittarius

Now you can look forward to an influx of bright and interesting new ideas. The Sun is about to enter your solar third house and that means constructive thinking and positive action. It is the start of a new working week and you should be able to find ways to make life sing. The only thing you might not manage is to improve much in a professional sense.

21 TUESDAY
Moon Age Day 24   Moon Sign Capricorn

Make today your own by turning directly away from routines and by looking for something exciting to do. Avoid tiring yourself early in the day and spread your energy evenly throughout the morning and afternoon. That way you will be quite happy to trip the light fantastic in the evening.

22 WEDNESDAY
Moon Age Day 25   Moon Sign Capricorn

Mundane and domestic matters might prove tiresome today, which is precisely why you are not involving yourself with them at all if you can help it. Aquarians who have tended to be off colour across the last week or so should now be noticing a definite improvement, with energy levels increasing all the time.

23 THURSDAY
Moon Age Day 26   Moon Sign Capricorn

There are people around now who have the ability to stimulate your mind simply by talking to you. It isn't out of the question that you will fall in love today, though as is so often the case for Aquarius, this is affection of the temporary sort and not to be confused with that necessary for a lifetime commitment.

24 FRIDAY
Moon Age Day 27   Moon Sign Aquarius

It should not be at all difficult to make headway now that the lunar high is here. You might find it difficult to create as many positive opportunities as you would wish in a financial sense, but when it comes to having a good time, you have fun coming out of your ears. No matter what your age your vitality should be at its highest level.

25 SATURDAY
Moon Age Day 28   Moon Sign Aquarius

The good trends continue, so much so that you know exactly what to do to get the right response from others. This should definitely not be a stay-at-home sort of weekend. On the contrary you need to get as much change as possible into your life – even if that means making some sort of impromptu journey or a last-minute break.

26 SUNDAY
Moon Age Day 29   Moon Sign Pisces

Avoid any tendency to be overbearing. With Mars in a position in your chart that can lead to you putting your ideas forward too strongly, extra care is necessary to ensure that this does not happen. You will not do yourself any good in the long run if you fail to use a degree of tact. Friends could be quite demanding.

27 MONDAY
Moon Age Day 0   Moon Sign Pisces

The planets send you a firm message now and it's to 'get cracking'! This would be a good day to capitalise on recent fresh starts. Don't make up your mind too quickly regarding current projects that mean taking rapid action straight away, though, and instead take time to analyse them carefully and properly before making a commitment.

28 TUESDAY
Moon Age Day 1   Moon Sign Aries

This should be a good period from a domestic perspective. Restrictions are few and far between. You have a strong desire to get out and about, though you are more likely to do so today in the company of family members. Give yourself credit for a success that is becoming more obvious with each passing day.

29 WEDNESDAY
Moon Age Day 2   Moon Sign Aries

It is true that you insist on being the centre of attention now. This is born of a sort of pride, which, as we know, quite often goes before a fall. Allow others to take the lead in situations that don't matter all that much. If you do, the same people will be far more willing to back you in matters that you see as being genuinely important.

30 THURSDAY
Moon Age Day 3   Moon Sign Taurus

There are plenty of light-hearted moments now and you have the chance to display your sense of humour to the world. Your confidence is not lacking, even if the ability to actually get where you want to be is somewhat restricted. You are able to arrange situations to suit your social life and should also find time for your family.

31 FRIDAY
Moon Age Day 4   Moon Sign Taurus

Don't allow yourself to become distracted with avenues that are not worth exploring. It appears you have some sort of idea in your head right now and will be chasing it for all you are worth. Make absolutely certain that it is practical and that it stands at least some chance of coming to fruition. If you don't, you are probably just wasting your time.

April

2017

Your Month at a Glance

⊕ = Opportunities are around   ● = Be on the defensive   ⬤ = Life is pretty ordinary

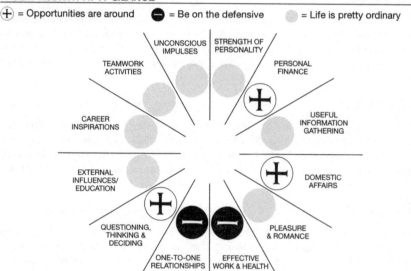

- UNCONSCIOUS IMPULSES
- STRENGTH OF PERSONALITY
- TEAMWORK ACTIVITIES
- PERSONAL FINANCE ⊕
- CAREER INSPIRATIONS
- USEFUL INFORMATION GATHERING
- EXTERNAL INFLUENCES/ EDUCATION
- DOMESTIC AFFAIRS ⊕
- QUESTIONING, THINKING & DECIDING ⊕
- PLEASURE & ROMANCE
- ONE-TO-ONE RELATIONSHIPS ⊖
- EFFECTIVE WORK & HEALTH ⊖

April Highs and Lows

Here I show you how the rhythms of the Moon will affect you this month. Like the tide, your energies and abilities will rise and fall with its pattern. When it is above the centre line, go for it, when it is below, you should be resting.

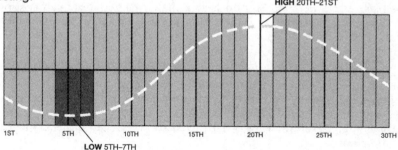

HIGH 20TH–21ST

1ST   5TH   10TH   15TH   20TH   25TH   30TH

LOW 5TH–7TH

65

1 SATURDAY
Moon Age Day 5   Moon Sign Gemini

With good social trends around, your ego may receive a boost. It seems as though you are very much in demand at the moment and this state of affairs is only going to become more obvious as the day wears on. Your communication skills are especially good and you know what it takes to make your friends laugh.

2 SUNDAY
Moon Age Day 6   Moon Sign Gemini

The drive to achieve is very strong and continues to increase markedly today and in the days ahead. This is going to be quite a month for many Aquarians, with successes coming thick and fast. Your energy and determination know no bounds and the desire to get ahead, particularly at home, is especially well marked.

3 MONDAY
Moon Age Day 7   Moon Sign Cancer

Where you are more or less certain to win out today is in attracting the material things of life. You won't want to spend all your time working and can afford to take some time out to enjoy yourself. If you find you are rather better off than you expected to be, then spend a pound or two. It will make you feel happy.

4 TUESDAY
Moon Age Day 8   Moon Sign Cancer

It is the quality of experiences that appeals to you at the moment and certainly not quantity. You have been burning the candle at both ends for some days and so should not be surprised if you suddenly find yourself collapsing into a heap. Socially speaking things are still good, relaxed encounters with friends works best.

5 WEDNESDAY
Moon Age Day 9   Moon Sign Leo

Various setbacks are more or less inevitable now that the lunar low is here. Keep up appearances by pretending to have a good time, even when this is not really the case at all. You do have a chance to get ahead at work; not because you are inherently successful at present, more because you don't mind putting in the hours.

6 THURSDAY
Moon Age Day 10   Moon Sign Leo

Your energy and general spirits might be low, which is why you will need to find some way right now to cheer yourself up. Keep away from negative types, or the sort of people who constantly make demands of you but offer nothing at all in return. Your confidence is still there, but rather buried for the moment.

7 FRIDAY
Moon Age Day 11   Moon Sign Leo

Your judgement regarding certain a personal decision may be askew and you can help yourself if you are willing to take on board the advice of someone in the know. It would also be wise to consult your partner if you want to change aspects of your personal life. If you charge ahead without thinking you may have cause to regret it.

8 SATURDAY
Moon Age Day 12   Moon Sign Virgo

Along comes a socially uplifting trend and a time when you find it easy to attract just the right sort of people into your life. Group-based activities are especially well highlighted at this time and it isn't hard for you to stand up and speak in public. On the contrary, you would welcome the opportunity.

9 SUNDAY
Moon Age Day 13   Moon Sign Virgo

With certain, specific emotional issues still uppermost in your mind, it could be somewhat awkward to concentrate on those things that you know you should be doing in a practical sense. Put your anxieties on the back burner. By the time you get round to looking at them again, hey presto they have disappeared.

10 MONDAY   ☿
Moon Age Day 14   Moon Sign Libra

Talks and general encounters with others ought to be part of what this Monday is about. Be willing to think ahead and maybe stay still in quiet contemplation for a few hours, even though the restless streak is still upon you. The more you mull things over today, the better you are likely to get on in the longer-term.

11 TUESDAY   ☿
Moon Age Day 15   Moon Sign Libra

There are pleasant encounters to be expected today, not least of all with people you haven't seen for some time. Catching up with the past is part of your present and seems to be quite important to you now. Avoid dull and boring routines if you possibly can because they hold nothing of interest for you at this time.

12 WEDNESDAY   ☿
Moon Age Day 16   Moon Sign Scorpio

There is something of the pioneer about you today, yet the desire to get new things up and running requires patience and balance, qualities that could be in rather short supply just for the moment. It would be better to restrict yourself to less demanding jobs in the workplace and to continue the search for fun once your time is your own.

13 THURSDAY ☿   *Moon Age Day 17   Moon Sign Scorpio*

This would be a good day for being on the move. You won't want to be held back by anything, not even relatives, some of whom are quite demanding at this time. Routines can be a bore, especially if they involve you spending long periods of time in the same place. Avoid them for now and instead, think big!

14 FRIDAY ☿   *Moon Age Day 18   Moon Sign Scorpio*

Home will seem to be the best place for you this Friday, though clearly you have responsibilities out there in the wider world and would be unlikely to shirk them. You are quite creative just now, so perhaps you will turn your mind to thinking about changes at home, or maybe take the opportunity to simply go shopping for clothes?

15 SATURDAY ☿   *Moon Age Day 19   Moon Sign Sagittarius*

You should jump at any opportunities that come along to travel. Don't be put off by people who tell you all the pitfalls of being on the move, especially if you are intending to go a long way. It's a great big world out there, and it looks particularly attractive and inviting to all Aquarian people at the moment.

16 SUNDAY ☿   *Moon Age Day 20   Moon Sign Sagittarius*

Trends suggest that you can expect a few setbacks when it comes to making decisions today. The problem is likely to be that everyone has a their own point of view and offers you different advice. It might be necessary to decide for yourself which path to follow, even if one or two people directly disagree with your conclusions.

17 MONDAY ☿   *Moon Age Day 21   Moon Sign Capricorn*

Places of entertainment are a must today. You need diversion and can find it in a host of different places. What wouldn't suit you at all right now would be to find yourself tied to a particular place or routine, to the exclusion of all else, which may be a problem on the average Monday. The most important thing today is to keep talking.

18 TUESDAY ☿   *Moon Age Day 22   Moon Sign Capricorn*

You will enjoy maintaining a high profile, especially in social settings. Your natural urge is to take a hands-on approach to almost any situation and you certainly will not be happy to let others live your life for you. Think seriously about a contract or other document you are asked to sign today, or at some time in the near future and weigh up its contents carefully.

19 WEDNESDAY ☿   *Moon Age Day 23   Moon Sign Capricorn*

Situations are looking rather harmonious today and you may even consider that life is somewhat dull. If this turns out to be the case you probably only have yourself to blame. In material matters and where decisions have to be made, now you should take the bull by the horns. Your decision-making is excellent now.

20 THURSDAY ☿   *Moon Age Day 24   Moon Sign Aquarius*

It's full steam ahead as all the positive influences in your chart come together to offer you a cracking day. Of course you cannot expect everyone to be on your side, but the majority of people who really count will help you out. Your confidence is strong and your earning potential should be especially good during this month's lunar high.

21 FRIDAY ☿   *Moon Age Day 25   Moon Sign Aquarius*

Most everyday issues should continue to go according to plan, without you having to interfere with them in any way. That leaves you free to progress in just about any manner you choose. Avoid pointless arguments with colleagues or friends. All you really want to do at the moment is to get on well with everyone.

22 SATURDAY ☿   *Moon Age Day 26   Moon Sign Pisces*

Assistance arrives from unexpected places, especially when it comes to any issue involving money. Meanwhile, you show a very social face to the world and can get on well with anyone, even with people who haven't been your cup of tea in the past. Plan now for some sort of excursion in the days ahead.

23 SUNDAY ☿   *Moon Age Day 27   Moon Sign Pisces*

Positive thinking can help enormously at present. Even if you encounter the odd setback today you will still be moving forward in a general sense. A growing desire to throw off the fetters of conventional thinking becomes apparent, though this is nothing too unusual for Aquarius. Decide on what you want from life and go for it.

24 MONDAY ☿   *Moon Age Day 28   Moon Sign Pisces*

A strong planetary emphasis on home and family is presented by the Sun, now in your solar fourth house. Although you may have slightly overlooked the needs and wants of loved ones for the last few days, you are less likely to do so in the three or four weeks that lie ahead of you. Prepare for much improved relations with your partner and loved ones.

25 TUESDAY ☿   *Moon Age Day 0   Moon Sign Aries*

There are plenty of interesting things happening today, most probably in association with your love life. In addition, the very real effort that others put in your behalf can make you feel generally good about yourself. If someone you know shares a confidence with you at present it must be carefully guarded, although this is generally good advice at any time.

26 WEDNESDAY ☿   *Moon Age Day 1   Moon Sign Aries*

You are likely to discover that it is impossible to please all of the people, all of the time. Despite this dawning realisation, it looks as though you will try to do so at some stage today. How can you help it? Conciliation and arbitration are hallmarks of your zodiac sign. Just be prepared, because there are a number of awkward people around at the moment.

27 THURSDAY ☿   *Moon Age Day 2   Moon Sign Taurus*

Practical progress, especially at work, proves easy enough to deal with. Avoid allowing others to pressurise you. This shouldn't be too much of a problem now but might prove to be more so in a few days. Start as you mean to go on and let people know just how far you are willing to bend in any given situation.

28 FRIDAY ☿   *Moon Age Day 3   Moon Sign Taurus*

Loved ones seek emotional assistance and you should be in a good position to help them significantly. Aquarius is in a listening mood and many of your efforts today are likely to be for the sake of those around you. Conforming to expectations in the workplace might not be particularly easy, but you should try to do so.

29 SATURDAY ☿   *Moon Age Day 4   Moon Sign Gemini*

That old friend of Aquarius – restlessness – could so easily pay you a visit now. In order to avoid this eventuality, you should keep busy and spend time thinking up new schemes that you find both stimulating and potentially rewarding. The most entertaining people at the moment appear to be friends who you have known for a long time.

30 SUNDAY ☿   *Moon Age Day 5   Moon Sign Gemini*

The more you mix with others, the greater is the amount of information that comes your way. You could be coming to the end of a particular activity or occupation which will leave you with more time to think up something new. People should be particularly helpful when it comes to work or financial matters.

May

2017

YOUR MONTH AT A GLANCE

⊕ = Opportunities are around   ⊖ = Be on the defensive   ● = Life is pretty ordinary

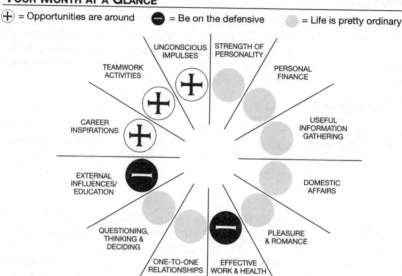

- UNCONSCIOUS IMPULSES
- STRENGTH OF PERSONALITY
- TEAMWORK ACTIVITIES
- PERSONAL FINANCE
- CAREER INSPIRATIONS
- USEFUL INFORMATION GATHERING
- EXTERNAL INFLUENCES/ EDUCATION
- DOMESTIC AFFAIRS
- QUESTIONING, THINKING & DECIDING
- PLEASURE & ROMANCE
- ONE-TO-ONE RELATIONSHIPS
- EFFECTIVE WORK & HEALTH

MAY HIGHS AND LOWS

Here I show you how the rhythms of the Moon will affect you this month. Like the tide, your energies and abilities will rise and fall with its pattern. When it is above the centre line, go for it, when it is below, you should be resting.

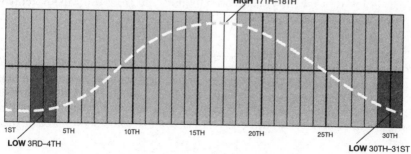

HIGH 17TH–18TH

1ST   5TH   10TH   15TH   20TH   25TH   30TH

LOW 3RD–4TH

LOW 30TH–31ST

I MONDAY ☿
Moon Age Day 6   Moon Sign Cancer

Though the general trends surrounding home and family seem to be as good now as they have been for quite a while, you may still find yourself to be rather restless on occasion today. Try to do something different and spend time with friends, some of whom should offer interesting ideas to help you break free of monotony.

2 TUESDAY ☿
Moon Age Day 7   Moon Sign Cancer

Where plans and schemes generally are concerned this is clearly a time to be taking an independent route. If you don't think others have the answers you need, now is the time to tell them so. There are certain responsibilities today that you can't shirk, so get them out of the way early in the day, then you will be free to go your own way.

3 WEDNESDAY ☿
Moon Age Day 8   Moon Sign Leo

Your energy levels are not high while the lunar low is around; that's a simple fact of life and there isn't too much point kicking against it. Keep yourself busy in quiet ways and enjoy the chance to take a break. What a great time this would be to walk in a beautiful garden and watch the flowers grow.

4 THURSDAY
Moon Age Day 9   Moon Sign Leo

Again today you could be feeling rather lacking in lustre and will be more inclined than usual to take the line of least resistance. However, even by the middle of the afternoon times will be changing, so for the moment watch and wait. Being patient isn't really your thing, and particularly not during this generally progressive period.

5 FRIDAY
Moon Age Day 10   Moon Sign Virgo

Certain initiatives you are thinking about right now are blocked by the negative attitudes and behaviour of others. It would be possible to bulldoze your ideas through but that won't be half as successful as fully explaining your point of view in a controlled manner. If you show patience and understanding, people will listen to you.

6 SATURDAY
Moon Age Day 11   Moon Sign Virgo

You want to keep abreast of social action right now and will not be too pleased if you discover that you are being loaded down with responsibilities you haven't asked for and don't want. Maybe it's time to tactfully speak your mind, although take great care if that is likely to mean upsetting someone you would rather keep sweet.

7 SUNDAY
Moon Age Day 12   Moon Sign Libra

The more unhurried elements of life are what count this Sunday. A rather contemplative Aquarian will greet this day, and your thoughtfulness is reflected in your general attitude towards others. Finding popularity is not difficult but are you really all that keen on yourself at present? If not, find the reasons.

8 MONDAY
Moon Age Day 13   Moon Sign Libra

This is the start of a new working week and a very good time to think about broadening your horizons in some way. Fresh fields and pastures new will appeal greatly and you certainly won't benefit from staying still and letting the world pass you by. It's time to take the world by storm, in precisely the way only an Aquarian can.

9 TUESDAY
Moon Age Day 14   Moon Sign Libra

Don't depend on an entirely positive response from others because trends suggest that you probably won't get one. This is a period during which you have to exhibit more than a little patience. Don't let this get you down. Once you have made up your mind to a specific course of action, especially in matters of the heart, stick to it.

10 WEDNESDAY
Moon Age Day 15   Moon Sign Scorpio

Getting securities into shape is something that might appeal around now. Don't spend all your time at home, though. Do what you can to get out and about, even if you are only making short, local journeys. Going to places where spring is in full and beautiful bloom should prove to be particularly interesting now.

11 THURSDAY
Moon Age Day 16   Moon Sign Scorpio

The domestic scene probably will not supply all the pleasure you are looking for right now. As a result you will feel the need to spread your wings. Everything about you says 'I want a change of scene', and if you can't get it then frustration is likely to follow. If you have been somewhat off-colour, take comfort from the fact that matters should improve very soon.

12 FRIDAY
Moon Age Day 17   Moon Sign Sagittarius

You enjoy being the centre of attention for much of the time today. There is a sense of fun around and a great desire to be where the action is. Of course this won't be possible all the time but you should be able to give a good account of yourself. Refuse to be cooped up and get plenty of fresh air now.

13 SATURDAY
Moon Age Day 18   Moon Sign Sagittarius

With high spirits and lots of energy you are ready to strike while the iron is hot. Important activities are on offer, though some friends or family members might be reluctant to get involved. Before you commit yourself do make sure that you are not going to offer any unintentional offence by taking an unpopular course of action.

14 SUNDAY
Moon Age Day 19   Moon Sign Sagittarius

Domestic matters take on a new importance and, at the same time, at least a part of your thoughts dwell in the past today. All sorts of minor issues come to the forefront of your mind and it is quite likely that you are overcrowding your intellect somewhat. Try to calm things down, learn a lesson from things gone by but avoid any tendency to melancholy.

15 MONDAY
Moon Age Day 20   Moon Sign Capricorn

At work there are challenges to deal with, a few of which could prove to be rather tedious. If you are not in work, or perhaps retired, the day offers different potential issues. Give and take is very important in personal attachments at present, even if it sometimes appears that you are doing most of the giving. Either way, a day to watch your step.

16 TUESDAY
Moon Age Day 21   Moon Sign Capricorn

In terms of communication today should work well for you. Little Mercury is positively placed in your chart, aiding your ability to say what you really think, but without giving offence to anyone in your vicinity. It looks as though most of the people you meet will consider you to be charming now.

17 WEDNESDAY
Moon Age Day 22   Moon Sign Aquarius

Now is a better time to get your own way with others. You don't have to work very hard to get where you want to be today and there is plenty of support on the way. Try to get as much variety into your life and enjoy the fact that you are rapidly becoming the centre of attention in your immediate circle.

18 THURSDAY
Moon Age Day 23   Moon Sign Aquarius

The general good luck is likely to continue now, thanks mainly to the continuing lunar high. Finances should strengthen, or at least you are using money wisely and frugally at the moment. Arguments at home will be wholly unnecessary now because you simply will not have to lose your temper in order to get what you need the most.

19 FRIDAY
Moon Age Day 24   Moon Sign Pisces

For those of you who are looking for advancement, or even a new career path, life could seem rather sluggish. Planetary trends now are geared more specifically towards your personal life and the less material elements of life. However, there is nothing to prevent you from thinking hard ahead of action in practical matters later.

20 SATURDAY
Moon Age Day 25   Moon Sign Pisces

There may be challenges in general life situations that tax you a little. Perhaps loved ones are particularly demanding this weekend or maybe you simply can't find your way forward through reams of red tape. It would be best to relax and to wait and see how the passing day changes your opinions.

21 SUNDAY
Moon Age Day 26   Moon Sign Pisces

Information you really need is likely to arrive today, either via your partner or from friends. Colleagues could prove to be slightly less helpful, perhaps because one or two of them feel you are flying too high at present and might represent a threat. In situations of confrontation you are, helpfully, presently slow to anger.

22 MONDAY
Moon Age Day 27   Moon Sign Aries

Almost everyone provides you with a friendly response at the start of this working week, so you should not have to try very hard to achieve positive objectives. Leave material concerns on the shelf for the moment because present trends reveal that you are in the mood to have some fun. Friends contribute to a growing feeling of personal confidence.

23 TUESDAY
Moon Age Day 28   Moon Sign Aries

Emotional and domestic matters are now increasing your sense of security and belonging. If Aquarians feel snug and warm inside their lives, outside matters tend to take care of themselves. Don't turn down a timely offer of assistance and make sure that you recognise that to accept would not be a sign of failure.

24 WEDNESDAY
Moon Age Day 29   Moon Sign Taurus

Family members have it in them to make you feel a great deal more comfortable today. Whether or not all of them choose to exercise this ability remains to be seen and is tied, in part, to your own attitude. Certainly in the case of younger relatives you may need to offer incentives that imply trust before they will open up to you.

25 THURSDAY
Moon Age Day 0   Moon Sign Taurus

The Sun is now in your solar fifth house, bringing extra incentive to your already positive social actions. When seen from the perspective of others you are a force to be reckoned with, even on those occasions when you don't have supreme confidence in your own abilities. Take advantage of this fact and push forward steadily.

26 FRIDAY
Moon Age Day 1   Moon Sign Gemini

The emphasis today is definitely on the domestic scene, so you may choose not to travel too far on this late spring Friday. Everything points to your private life being positively highlighted and many Aquarians will be in a position to enjoy the fruits of love and romance at the moment.

27 SATURDAY
Moon Age Day 2   Moon Sign Gemini

You have a natural curiosity and a real desire to broaden your horizons. This means you find yourself with another day that responds well to changes of scenery. Give and take proves to be important in personal matters but you will always get your own way in the end, and without upsetting any apple carts.

28 SUNDAY
Moon Age Day 3   Moon Sign Cancer

There could be pressures coming along in your social life, mainly born out of boredom if you have to do the same old things. It's time to ring the changes, even though to do so won't please everyone. The fact is though, that under the present trends in your chart, the individualist within you simply has to show its face as soon as possible.

29 MONDAY
Moon Age Day 4   Moon Sign Cancer

Though the pace of events is hurried, particularly at work, you will still find the time to socialise and to look at romance in a bigger way than has been possible for a few days. There are some great compliments coming your way at present, though you will have to pay attention if you don't want to miss them.

30 TUESDAY
Moon Age Day 5   Moon Sign Leo

Whatever you decide to take on board today, remember that your energy level is not going to be very high. It might be best to stay out of the limelight and to spend as many hours as you can doing something quiet. Personal relationships should be going well, though, and will be broadly unaffected by the lunar low.

31 WEDNESDAY
Moon Age Day 6   Moon Sign Leo

Another generally quiet sort of day and certainly not one during which you should take on jobs you know will be contentious or difficult. There is plenty of time after tomorrow to get on with whatever you wish but for the moment, be content to stay in company you know, avoiding unnecessary risks.

June

2017

YOUR MONTH AT A GLANCE

⊕ = Opportunities are around ⚫ = Be on the defensive ⚪ = Life is pretty ordinary

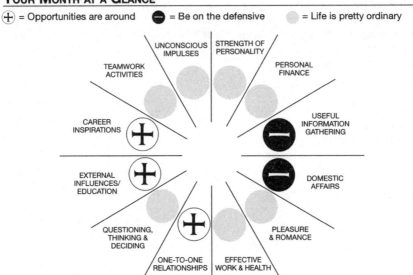

UNCONSCIOUS IMPULSES
STRENGTH OF PERSONALITY
TEAMWORK ACTIVITIES
PERSONAL FINANCE
CAREER INSPIRATIONS
USEFUL INFORMATION GATHERING
EXTERNAL INFLUENCES/ EDUCATION
DOMESTIC AFFAIRS
QUESTIONING, THINKING & DECIDING
PLEASURE & ROMANCE
ONE-TO-ONE RELATIONSHIPS
EFFECTIVE WORK & HEALTH

JUNE HIGHS AND LOWS

Here I show you how the rhythms of the Moon will affect you this month. Like the tide, your energies and abilities will rise and fall with its pattern. When it is above the centre line, go for it, when it is below, you should be resting.

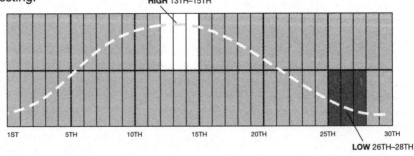

HIGH 13TH–15TH

| 1ST | 5TH | 10TH | 15TH | 20TH | 25TH | 30TH |

LOW 26TH–28TH

78

1 THURSDAY
Moon Age Day 7   Moon Sign Virgo

You want to shine out personally today and there is very little to prevent you from doing so. A few uninteresting jobs should be dealt with early in the day and then you can concentrate on what pleases you. If certain aspects of the past come back to haunt you at present, simply smile and carry on regardless.

2 FRIDAY
Moon Age Day 8   Moon Sign Virgo

Self-reliance is very important at this time. All the same, what matters the most right now is not what others can do for you but rather what you can accomplish for them. The deeper and more spiritual side of your nature is now beginning to demonstrate itself. Don't be surprised if you are very popular right now.

3 SATURDAY
Moon Age Day 9   Moon Sign Virgo

You won't get quite as much peace and quiet as you could be looking for today, though in the end you probably won't worry too much about it. Trends suggest that people you haven't seen for ages are likely to come back into your life at present, and they might bring some interesting ideas and possibilities with them.

4 SUNDAY
Moon Age Day 10   Moon Sign Libra

The most rewarding moments you experience today are associated in some way with leisure and pleasure. You won't be too keen to be tied down with boring routines all the time. On the contrary you will actively look for the new and unusual. If you can't find it, then simply keep searching and don't become frustrated.

5 MONDAY
Moon Age Day 11   Moon Sign Libra

A little privacy goes a long way, even though you prefer right now to be in the social limelight. Stay away from cloying people and stifling situations. You may feel that you are being suffocated by convention, especially if you are a young Aquarian, but you don't have any real choice except to go with the flow, at least sometimes.

6 THURSDAY
Moon Age Day 12   Moon Sign Scorpio

Though you are putting a great deal of energy into getting things done, it may seem as though others are merely throwing obstacles in your path. Do your best to see their point of view because this may not be the case and they could have an important message to impart. Leave boring routines to types who appear to relish them.

7 WEDNESDAY
Moon Age Day 13   Moon Sign Scorpio

Beware of pushing ahead with new ambitions before you have really investigated situations. This is especially relevant where money is concerned. Actually this isn't a particularly good time for speculation of any sort and you would be well advised to put a curb on your spending until you have sorted your mind out.

8 THURSDAY
Moon Age Day 14   Moon Sign Sagittarius

It is especially easy to do more than one thing at a time today. This isn't a difficult matter for the sign of Aquarius at the best of times, but take heed of this word of warning: more haste, less speed. Do not rush at things and overtax yourself or you will end up having to repeat the same task umpteen times before you get it right.

9 FRIDAY
Moon Age Day 15   Moon Sign Sagittarius

Sorting matters out as far as your personal life is concerned may take up at least part of your time today. Try not to give into pressure, simply for the sake of a peaceful life and keep pushing towards success in projects that are close to your own heart. Although you might tire easily right now you are methodical and yet easy-going.

10 SATURDAY
Moon Age Day 16   Moon Sign Sagittarius

From a personal point of view this could easily turn out to be the best day of the week. Once the weekend necessities are out of the way you can turn your attention towards the lighter side of life. Spending time with your nearest and dearest should prove rewarding but you will find time for friends too.

11 SUNDAY
Moon Age Day 17   Moon Sign Capricorn

Co-operative ventures allow you to greet Sunday as you mean to go on, in a sociable frame of mind and happy to get on with just about anyone. There are a few miseries about but there's very little you can do about them. Don't allow yourself to be dragged into disputes that you personally find ridiculous and unnecessary.

12 MONDAY
Moon Age Day 18   Moon Sign Capricorn

It could look from your point of view as if others are getting ahead much better than you are. The Moon in your solar twelfth house gives you a slightly distorted perspective but it won't take you as deeply into yourself as it sometimes does. Although this is a good time to pace yourself it is not an interlude that requires you to stop altogether.

13 TUESDAY
Moon Age Day 19   Moon Sign Aquarius

The general trends are good overall today, especially in any situation that involves you taking the bull by the horns. You can't leave things to chance but should discover that you have enough going for you to take it upon yourself to make life easy. Good luck is certainly on your side, so a small flutter might be in order, if you can spare a little cash.

14 WEDNESDAY
Moon Age Day 20   Moon Sign Aquarius

There are great opportunities to make gains today, especially in a financial sense. It appears that you see the future as if it were already mapped out for you and that can be useful. Hunches work out as you would expect and even people who haven't shown you any particular preference in the past should do so now.

15 THURSDAY
Moon Age Day 21   Moon Sign Aquarius

Avoid misunderstandings by stating your case from the start. Some relaxation is possible later in the day and although you will be busy for a good deal of the time, you find ways to make your work less of a chore. Start to look at something particularly interesting to do across the coming weekend.

16 FRIDAY
Moon Age Day 22   Moon Sign Pisces

Exciting social encounters can be expected today. Stay away from what you see as being pointless rules and regulations because these will only annoy you. Friends should prove to be both supportive and very interesting as the day wears on. With exceptional strength of personality, you will not retreat from any challenge.

17 SATURDAY
Moon Age Day 23   Moon Sign Pisces

A heavily competitive element comes along now, forcing you to look at even existing circumstances in a radically different way. You won't want to lose at any game or sport, whilst in terms of career prospects your mind is working overtime. All the same, find a few hours to put competition aside and enjoy yourself.

18 SUNDAY
Moon Age Day 24   Moon Sign Aries

Matters should proceed very much according to plan today, which might mean that your presence on the home front is not really necessary. All the more reason to get out of the house and to go somewhere interesting. You are a cultured type, so perhaps you could visit a historic ruin, or take a long walk in a scenic place?

19 MONDAY
Moon Age Day 25   Moon Sign Aries

Despite your best efforts, it could appear that you are missing out somehow in the career stakes. This would be an ideal time for a reappraisal. If necessary, seek out some professional advice and certainly don't assume that you already know the answer to any problem. Plan your strategy carefully in any area.

20 TUESDAY
Moon Age Day 26   Moon Sign Taurus

If financial stability is on your mind right now, you could find ways and means to improve the situation. You may need to follow up on a couple of leads and, perhaps, to read some printed matter. However, with a good deal of thought and a little action, your finances could look very much stronger before long.

21 WEDNESDAY
Moon Age Day 27   Moon Sign Taurus

A successful time can be expected in affairs of the heart, whether these are of the lifelong variety or simply temporary assignations. Conforming to the expectations others have of you, especially certain family members won't be too easy, and you may need a little tolerance, particularly when dealing with younger people.

22 THURSDAY
Moon Age Day 28   Moon Sign Gemini

There is plenty of energy present at the moment to allow you to break through barriers that might have looked high and wide indeed in the recent past. You might be left wondering why you were intimidated in the first place and you will definitely be sharpening your persuasive skills and general intellect today. The planets say you should go far.

23 FRIDAY
Moon Age Day 29   Moon Sign Gemini

Try to keep things on an even keel at work and avoid allowing yourself to become distracted by matters you cannot control. Be prepared to accept some timely help and advice, especially when it comes from the direction of someone you care about deeply. Confronting certain issues might not work too well today.

24 SATURDAY
Moon Age Day 0   Moon Sign Cancer

You can expect an eventful social life, together with consistently improving trends in deeper attachments. Aquarians who are now starting a new romantic relationship are likely to find it going from strength to strength. In any area of life, when decisions have to be made, utilise your intuition and gut reactions.

25 SUNDAY
Moon Age Day 1   Moon Sign Cancer

Today should bring you plenty of opportunities to hog the limelight, though you may be tiring of having to smile so much. You won't be stuck for an answer to any question, and this is definitely the best time to put yourself on display. If there are any limitations on your nature during present trends, these are probably self-created.

26 MONDAY
Moon Age Day 2   Moon Sign Leo

Though your dealings with others in social settings could be somewhat strained, there are always those amongst your friends who rate you highly. Practically speaking this is a time of high achievement. Avoid pointless and unnecessary discussions about situations that don't interest you and which you cannot alter.

27 TUESDAY
Moon Age Day 3   Moon Sign Leo

Put any major issues on the back burner and prepare yourself for a day, or even two, that could easily turn out to be quiet. This is no bad thing and will allow you some time to think about yourself and the projects you are presently planning. Although you may not feel highly charged in a social sense, there should be offers about.

28 WEDNESDAY
Moon Age Day 4   Moon Sign Leo

Success comes at the moment partly through being well organised. You can fall down only if you haven't dealt with every possible eventuality. Don't let opportunities slip simply because you haven't prepared yourself properly. This would also be a good time to instigate new business partnerships.

29 THURSDAY
Moon Age Day 5   Moon Sign Virgo

It is possible that you will discover other people's true feelings about you around this time. In the main you ought to be delighted but your ego can easily be dented if not all responses are exactly as you would wish them to be. You may have to come to terms with the fact that not everyone loves you.

30 FRIDAY
Moon Age Day 6   Moon Sign Virgo

Your attention might be turned towards financial matters today. Expect better-than-average success early in the day, though there may be something of a temporary decline from the middle of the afternoon onwards. Luckily, finding the means to enjoy yourself is presently second nature so it should be easy to switch your attention away from the world of finance.

2017

YOUR MONTH AT A GLANCE

(+) = Opportunities are around   ● = Be on the defensive   ◯ = Life is pretty ordinary

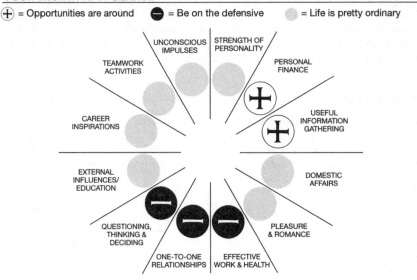

STRENGTH OF PERSONALITY

UNCONSCIOUS IMPULSES

TEAMWORK ACTIVITIES

PERSONAL FINANCE

CAREER INSPIRATIONS

USEFUL INFORMATION GATHERING

EXTERNAL INFLUENCES/ EDUCATION

DOMESTIC AFFAIRS

QUESTIONING, THINKING & DECIDING

PLEASURE & ROMANCE

ONE-TO-ONE RELATIONSHIPS

EFFECTIVE WORK & HEALTH

JULY HIGHS AND LOWS

Here I show you how the rhythms of the Moon will affect you this month. Like the tide, your energies and abilities will rise and fall with its pattern. When it is above the centre line, go for it, when it is below, you should be resting.

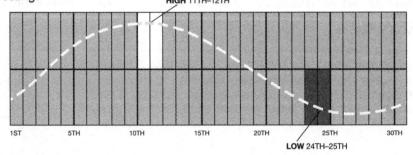

HIGH 11TH–12TH

1ST   5TH   10TH   15TH   20TH   25TH   30TH

LOW 24TH–25TH

84

1 SATURDAY
Moon Age Day 7   Moon Sign Libra

If you can manage to slow down the pace of life somewhat this weekend, then so much the better. Don't let yourself get so busy that you fail to see the wood for the trees. Weekends are partly about relaxing, which doesn't mean dropping one lot of responsibilities so that you can concentrate on another, it means taking a physical and mental break.

2 SUNDAY
Moon Age Day 8   Moon Sign Libra

A time to be wary, because you might be up against some strident views, most of which are coming from the direction of people you associate with on a day-to-day basis. Take life steadily today, think things through carefully and don't allow yourself to become flustered by issues that normally would not bother you in the slightest.

3 MONDAY
Moon Age Day 9   Moon Sign Scorpio

Make the most of beneficial highlights that come along, particularly at work. Good results come from practical efforts and you have what it takes to make the most of all situations today. Love and romance are principal amongst your concerns today and you should also find popularity amongst your peers.

4 TUESDAY
Moon Age Day 10   Moon Sign Scorpio

Personal contacts with co-workers look as if they are going to turn out better today than has been the case for quite some time. It could be that some sort of antagonism has been evident and it is now possible to put that behind you. With generally good trends all round, friends should be disarming and especially warm right now.

5 WEDNESDAY
Moon Age Day 11   Moon Sign Scorpio

The current planetary focus is on work and you are kept very much on the move today, whether or not you are actually holding down a position at the moment. Socially speaking you seem content to have a good time, though there is a quieter side to your nature that shows itself on occasion at present.

6 THURSDAY
Moon Age Day 12   Moon Sign Sagittarius

You should enjoy social discussions of almost any sort now. Your concern for others is strong though it is likely that this is misplaced as family members are faring better now than seems to have been the case for the last few days. At work you are aware that there is no shortcut to success, so simply keep ploughing on regardless.

7 FRIDAY
Moon Age Day 13   Moon Sign Sagittarius

Positive highlights in relationships can make this a very good day on the personal front. At the same time you are overtaken by a distinctly nostalgic mood; one that can take your mind far back into the past. A strong boost to social matters, together with progressive trends might turn your mind towards sport.

8 SATURDAY
Moon Age Day 14   Moon Sign Capricorn

At work you could be a winner, and this trend is set to last for a while. This is only really relevant right now if you are a weekend worker, otherwise you will be putting your efforts into your home and social life. Concern for the underdog is high in the list of Aquarian priorities at this point in time.

9 SUNDAY
Moon Age Day 15   Moon Sign Capricorn

A variety of new interests now allow you to get the very best from life. Try not to become overanxious about situations that don't really matter at all. Cultivate your more creative side and seek out intellectual stimulation instead. Soap operas and computer games won't offer you as much as cultural pursuits on this Sunday.

10 MONDAY
Moon Age Day 16   Moon Sign Capricorn

A variety of different sorts of news and views should be coming your way at the beginning of this working week. Your confidence is not hard to find when you need it the most but you should be prepared to have to work especially hard for something you have definitely set your mind on having. Toeing the expected line isn't always easy now.

11 TUESDAY
Moon Age Day 17   Moon Sign Aquarius

The time comes along for a completely confident approach, assisted greatly by the presence of the Moon in your own zodiac sign. If there are things you are bursting to say, now is the time. With more than your fair share of good luck at this time, you can afford to chance your arm a little more than usual.

12 WEDNESDAY
Moon Age Day 18   Moon Sign Aquarius

The good times should be continuing, probably despite a little news that looks less than favourable initially. Stay away from boring jobs and get out there in the wide world as much as possible today. The more you mix and mingle, the greater will be your ability to make friends and influence others.

13 THURSDAY
Moon Age Day 19   Moon Sign Pisces

This is one of your very best days for freely pursuing personal interests and desires. Today blows a breeze of change into your life and you ought to wake feeling generally optimistic and only too willing to put in whatever effort is necessary in order to gain your most cherished objectives.

14 FRIDAY
Moon Age Day 20   Moon Sign Pisces

When it comes to fulfilling the expectations that others have of you, the chances are that you are second to none right now. Convincing people of your sincerity in almost any situation should not be at all difficult. Get some rest if you have been burning the candle at both ends, though without killing your social life stone dead.

15 SATURDAY
Moon Age Day 21   Moon Sign Aries

The pursuit of personal freedom is uppermost in your mind, as it often turns out to be for Aquarians. There is something you are not getting at present and though the thing itself might not be important, the principle almost certainly is. Give and take is important in all areas, but especially when it comes to friendship.

16 SUNDAY
Moon Age Day 22   Moon Sign Aries

You now find yourself in a period during which all practical matters should push ahead quite nicely. Difficulties associated with relationships are less likely at this time and you can rely on friends to offer the sort of support you need when you want it the most. This should be a good Sunday where you are feeling settled and comfortable.

17 MONDAY
Moon Age Day 23   Moon Sign Aries

Your good ideas and reputation for ingenuity are called into play this week. People you might never have suspected of keeping in touch with your opinions will be sounding you out now and might be willing to offer you something in return for your input. Romance looks fine too, perhaps with a surprise or two on the way.

18 TUESDAY
Moon Age Day 24   Moon Sign Taurus

Your social life looks good today, though it may not do if you allow yourself to get involved in disputes that shouldn't be taking place at all. Try to stay neutral if possible, even playing an honest broker amongst arguing friends. The events now are interesting but you have to steer a careful course if you don't want to become involved in difficult matters.

19 WEDNESDAY
Moon Age Day 25 Moon Sign Taurus

There are dangers right now in trying to make the world run the way you wish. It would be far better for the moment to realise that your own opinions belong just to you and that others may not share them. Mistakes will be made today but you are good at putting forward a loss-limitation exercise.

20 THURSDAY
Moon Age Day 26 Moon Sign Gemini

With the Moon still just in your solar tenth house, practical matters should be going well enough, though it is possible that you are taking a less than serious approach to specific events in your life. You certainly exhibit a devil-may-care attitude of the sort that is typified by Aquarius when it is not really paying attention.

21 FRIDAY
Moon Age Day 27 Moon Sign Gemini

There is a definite tendency towards acquisition at this end of this week and this might cause you to focus on the wrong things. Whilst you can make money in one way, it is likely to be slipping through your fingers in others. Your confidence in your own ability remains intact but the weekend ahead could call for a more conservative approach.

22 SATURDAY
Moon Age Day 28 Moon Sign Cancer

What happens in the practical world today could prove to be quite decisive. Maybe you are making significant changes at home or expecting family members to behave in specific ways? Be aware that all your actions and plans could come to very little unless you make it plain that you have your finger on important pulses.

23 SUNDAY
Moon Age Day 0 Moon Sign Cancer

Planetary trends are shifting all the time now and today you could find yourself faced with a day during which good co-operation is the key to success. Being at the head of things isn't that important for the moment but rather you should concentrate on making yourself available as a valued part of a team.

24 MONDAY
Moon Age Day 1 Moon Sign Leo

A lull patch commences with the arrival of the lunar low. Although you are hardly likely to feel depressed during such a generally positive time in your life, there will be some setbacks if you insist on keeping up your general speed. Create a little space for yourself today and, having done so, sit in it and relax.

25 TUESDAY
Moon Age Day 2   Moon Sign Leo

Although this will be another day that is less than inspiring, this Tuesday shows you to have slightly more influence than was probably the case yesterday. Friends should be willing to help you out and have some interesting news to impart when it matters the most. Slowly but surely, you climb out of your little quiet spell.

26 WEDNESDAY
Moon Age Day 3   Moon Sign Virgo

Some of your efforts in the outside world could slow down somewhat, leaving you feeling that you are still in a lull. Actually this isn't the case and one good thing about today is that you are very thoughtful and therefore likely to achieve more. Don't worry unduly about the apparent wayward behaviour of younger family members, things should come good in the end.

27 THURSDAY
Moon Age Day 4   Moon Sign Virgo

Relationships and personal encounters prosper under today's trends. The Sun has entered your solar seventh house. As a result, you may fare slightly less well for the next month in terms of material gains but get on much better in all social or personal encounters. You should be able to strike a good balance.

28 FRIDAY
Moon Age Day 5   Moon Sign Libra

Don't settle for second best today, either from yourself or others. You really can afford to push situations now, even though you might have a nagging doubt that you are going too far. The true originality of your zodiac sign shines out like the sun. That means some people will love you – but others won't care for you at all.

29 SATURDAY
Moon Age Day 6   Moon Sign Libra

Don't take no for an answer in situations about which you are absolutely certain. At the same time, try to show a high degree of tact and diplomacy. Not everyone is equally easy to deal with and in any situation it would be quite sensible to listen carefully to what others have to say before you speak out.

30 SUNDAY
Moon Age Day 7   Moon Sign Libra

Trends suggest that you are now bringing certain projects near to completion. This might not be too easy to achieve on a Sunday if the subject matter is professional, but you are also doing well in terms of family-based schemes. Your co-operative skills are second to none, leaving you well able to get your head together with others.

31 MONDAY

Moon Age Day 8   Moon Sign Scorpio

Be open and ready for new input at this time, especially from people who have been trying for a while to become part of your inner circle. Things may be changing somewhat in terms of the people you mix with on a day-to-day basis and there is a definite feeling of 'off with the old and on with the new'.

August

2017

Your Month at a Glance

⊕ = Opportunities are around ● = Be on the defensive ● = Life is pretty ordinary

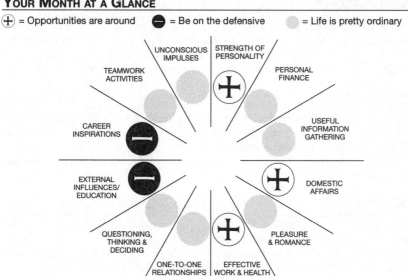

- UNCONSCIOUS IMPULSES
- STRENGTH OF PERSONALITY
- TEAMWORK ACTIVITIES
- PERSONAL FINANCE
- CAREER INSPIRATIONS
- USEFUL INFORMATION GATHERING
- EXTERNAL INFLUENCES/ EDUCATION
- DOMESTIC AFFAIRS
- QUESTIONING, THINKING & DECIDING
- PLEASURE & ROMANCE
- ONE-TO-ONE RELATIONSHIPS
- EFFECTIVE WORK & HEALTH

August Highs and Lows

Here I show you how the rhythms of the Moon will affect you this month. Like the tide, your energies and abilities will rise and fall with its pattern. When it is above the centre line, go for it, when it is below, you should be resting.

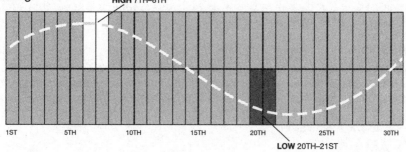

HIGH 7TH–8TH

LOW 20TH–21ST

1ST 5TH 10TH 15TH 20TH 25TH 30TH

91

1 TUESDAY
Moon Age Day 9   Moon Sign Scorpio

Some professional requirements can be tricky today and you will have to think them through as carefully as you can. Make sure you are getting enough rest at this time and don't expect more of yourself than is reasonable. There is help there for the taking but you will have to admit you are struggling in order to get it.

2 WEDNESDAY
Moon Age Day 10   Moon Sign Sagittarius

Someone very close to you may well do you a great service today and you will want to find ways and means to pay them back. Attitude is all-important when you are dealing with people who can be difficult. It is essential to remain patient and not to push situations more than is strictly necessary.

3 THURSDAY
Moon Age Day 11   Moon Sign Sagittarius

Avoid any impulse buying today and only spend money when you know for certain that you are getting a genuine bargain. Don't be too quick to take offence over remarks that probably were not directed at you in any case and be willing to eat humble pie if you do get hold of the wrong end of the stick in any conversation.

4 FRIDAY
Moon Age Day 12   Moon Sign Sagittarius

There is wonderful company out there at present and all you have to do is set out to find it. Keep a sense of proportion when you are dealing with people who have big ideas but perhaps not the follow-through to put them into action. Your help in a situation like this could be invaluable – come to think of it, this may be the start of a stunning double-act.

5 SATURDAY
Moon Age Day 13   Moon Sign Capricorn

It's time to get yourself well organised. If you really want to make the best of this period, the stars say that you must think well ahead and not be afraid to take some considered decisions this weekend. It might mean taking some things at a slower pace than you would like but as long as you are thorough, you should make gains.

6 SUNDAY
Moon Age Day 14   Moon Sign Capricorn

Not a day to allow yourself to get down in the dumps about anything. You need to remain sure of yourself and confident in whatever you are doing. It might be the case that not everything is going to go your way today but rest assured that help is at hand and that there will be more productive days to come in the week ahead.

7 MONDAY
Moon Age Day 15   Moon Sign Aquarius

Now comes a chance to put longed-for plans and ambitions into action. This is very much your day but the outcome depends entirely on the amount of effort you are willing to put in. This won't be a problem at all because you are raring to go. Try to stay cool, calm and collected even on those occasions when you are very nervous inside.

8 TUESDAY
Moon Age Day 16   Moon Sign Aquarius

Put your persuasive powers to the test and don't be afraid to ask for what you want. With a little cheek and very good communication skills it is highly unlikely that anyone will refuse your reasonable requests. Money matters ought to improve now and there is even the possibility of a small windfall at some stage during the day.

9 WEDNESDAY
Moon Age Day 17   Moon Sign Pisces

This is a time when you simply love to be the centre of attention. Don't be surprised if you discover that you have some unexpected admirers. It won't be long before one or two of them are making their feelings abundantly clear. The only way that this could become a problem is if you are too naive to pick up the signals.

10 THURSDAY
Moon Age Day 18   Moon Sign Pisces

A strong drive to achieve, which has been such a part of your outlook on life over the last couple of weeks is still in place. You can't expect to have everything you want at present, though you should be in possession of most of what you actually need. There's a subtle difference, as you will realise if you just stop to think for a while.

11 FRIDAY
Moon Age Day 19   Moon Sign Pisces

Your desire to make important changes won't be without something of a struggle at the moment. Still, it's worth putting in that extra bit of effort if what you get out of it at the end improves your life. Stand by to receive some promising remarks from individuals who are in an excellent position to offer you a boost.

12 SATURDAY
Moon Age Day 20   Moon Sign Aries

Get a strong sense of movement into your life this weekend by keeping going, even when others are falling by the wayside. Energy is there when you need it the most, though you won't be against taking some time to put your feet up either. Financial gains are by no means guaranteed at this time but they are likely.

13 SUNDAY ☿ *Moon Age Day 21   Moon Sign Aries*

Material restrictions could force you to cut back on one or two things, though probably not for long. In a way it doesn't matter because what you want most in life at the moment cannot be purchased with any amount of cash. Your search is for personal happiness and there is a good chance you are going to find it, in part at least.

14 MONDAY ☿ *Moon Age Day 22   Moon Sign Taurus*

If you want to make the most of present social trends, you have to put in that extra bit of effort that can mean success. What doesn't come easily at present is conforming to the expectations of others. At the end of the day you have to be certain that what you are doing is right for you and put aside concerns regarding what those around you are thinking.

15 TUESDAY ☿ *Moon Age Day 23   Moon Sign Taurus*

Current influences suggest that this is an ideal time to think seriously about life and to make some necessary changes, if appropriate. Any alterations need to take place first of all in your mind and you won't move mountains in the real world until you have done so inside yourself. It really is a case of 'think it done and it can be done' right now.

16 WEDNESDAY ☿ *Moon Age Day 24   Moon Sign Gemini*

Financial planning undertaken now is likely to work out well. You have a very astute head on your shoulders and are also in a good position to see a host of different possibilities and strategies around this time. Aquarius is both confident and comfortable at the moment, and it definitely shows.

17 THURSDAY ☿ *Moon Age Day 25   Moon Sign Gemini*

Although it is clear you are looking for a high degree of personal freedom right now, you need to get important jobs out of the way before you think about taking a break. Don't be inclined to sit on the fence in issues you know to be important. Even if it means disagreeing with a friend, you have to speak your mind.

18 FRIDAY ☿ *Moon Age Day 26   Moon Sign Cancer*

Joint financial endeavours and co-operative ventures generally are well accented right now. Your intuitive powers are at their peak, allowing you to weigh up any given situation almost instantly. With a slight change of emphasis, people now see you as someone who is good at talking, rather than a contentious individual.

19 SATURDAY ☿   *Moon Age Day 27   Moon Sign Cancer*

If you had been planning on taking a chance in any romantic sense, now is the time to do it. Winning others round to your point of view, even beyond personal attachments ought to be quite easy. Fortune favours the brave and the planets tell us that you will have more than a little courage on show after next Monday.

20 SUNDAY ☿   *Moon Age Day 28   Moon Sign Leo*

This is not the best time to expect to get your own way in everything. Your perspectives are somewhat obscured by the presence of the lunar low. Rather than trying to do too much in a practical or material sense, perhaps you should spend at least a part of Sunday doing something that pleases only you.

21 MONDAY ☿   *Moon Age Day 29   Moon Sign Leo*

If you push yourself too hard today, you are likely to run out of steam very quickly indeed. Settle for some relaxation, plus the chance to look ahead and to do some prior planning. Everyone needs to recharge their batteries once in a while and although you hardly accept the fact, Aquarius is no different.

22 TUESDAY ☿   *Moon Age Day 0   Moon Sign Virgo*

The Moon moves on and this is a good time for getting down to business. You are clearly in a position to know what is best for you and could also have a good idea about what would suit your partner. Although you may appear to be slightly more timid today, in reality you are probably only showing necessary caution.

23 WEDNESDAY ☿   *Moon Age Day 1   Moon Sign Virgo*

Doing things in pairs could be quite good fun now. Co-operative ventures work best for you, no matter if these are professional partnerships at work, or later in the day when you can get to grips with personal attachments. You won't be everyone's cup of tea today, but the people who really matter to you are clearly on your side.

24 THURSDAY ☿   *Moon Age Day 2   Moon Sign Virgo*

You need to do more of your own thing today, as opposed to pleasing others all the time. This isn't really selfish, and even if it could be considered so, you do have the right to put your full focus on your own life and issues sometimes. Avoid family rows, especially since you are not the one who is starting them.

25 FRIDAY ☿ *Moon Age Day 3   Moon Sign Libra*

There is a continued accent on work and material considerations, so much so that you might find it difficult to spend any time doing exactly what you want. When you do have free hours, you are likely to spend a good proportion of them supporting other people, particularly friends who are having difficulties.

26 SATURDAY ☿ *Moon Age Day 4   Moon Sign Libra*

Today could turn out to be a good deal more exciting than you had expected. If you work on a Saturday, look out for a chance to gain new power or responsibility. However, if you have the weekend to yourself, you need to think about making changes to your social life and maybe even taking a few calculated risks.

27 SUNDAY ☿ *Moon Age Day 5   Moon Sign Scorpio*

Practical situations demand your attention much more now than they have recently and it is a fact that you won't have as much time today to concentrate on personal issues or the concerns of your friends. It would be quite possible for you to get yourself into something of a panic now if you try to take on too much.

28 MONDAY ☿ *Moon Age Day 6   Moon Sign Scorpio*

Getting along with others should be very easy as this new working week gets started. This isn't usually difficult for you in any case, though there have been a few occasions in the recent past when you haven't been quite as accommodating as usual. You may have to spread tasks out in order to get them done properly.

29 TUESDAY ☿ *Moon Age Day 7   Moon Sign Sagittarius*

What you hear from others can be of great use to you at present, so it is definitely worthwhile keeping your ears open today. That shouldn't be too much of a problem because Aquarius is one of the best dealers in gossip to be found anywhere within the zodiac. Look out for small financial gains at some point during the day.

30 WEDNESDAY ☿ *Moon Age Day 8   Moon Sign Sagittarius*

Trends suggest that this might be a period of time during which you will want to restructure elements of your life that you feel are not going the way you would wish. Instead of spending too much money today, plan how you can get more. The time for really spoiling yourself comes later, so for now work hard.

31 THURSDAY ☿

Moon Age Day 9   Moon Sign Sagittarius

What matters about today is eliciting the right sort of assistance for whatever you are planning. Your astute nature and strong intuition can be brought into play and your decisions will now be quite considered. Routine tasks are undertaken easily but there is a part of you that feels the strong need for some change and, perhaps, travel.

September

2017

YOUR MONTH AT A GLANCE

⊕ = Opportunities are around ● = Be on the defensive ◯ = Life is pretty ordinary

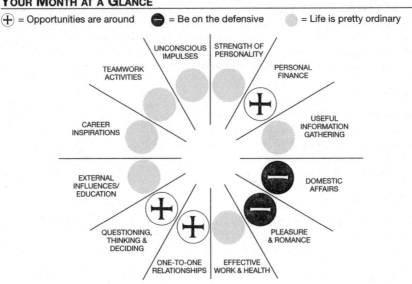

- STRENGTH OF PERSONALITY
- PERSONAL FINANCE
- USEFUL INFORMATION GATHERING
- DOMESTIC AFFAIRS
- PLEASURE & ROMANCE
- EFFECTIVE WORK & HEALTH
- ONE-TO-ONE RELATIONSHIPS
- QUESTIONING, THINKING & DECIDING
- EXTERNAL INFLUENCES/ EDUCATION
- CAREER INSPIRATIONS
- TEAMWORK ACTIVITIES
- UNCONSCIOUS IMPULSES

SEPTEMBER HIGHS AND LOWS

Here I show you how the rhythms of the Moon will affect you this month. Like the tide, your energies and abilities will rise and fall with its pattern. When it is above the centre line, go for it, when it is below, you should be resting.

HIGH 3RD–5TH

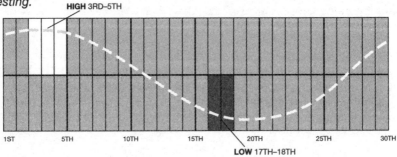

1ST   5TH   10TH   15TH   20TH   25TH   30TH

LOW 17TH–18TH

1 FRIDAY ☿ *Moon Age Day 10 Moon Sign Capricorn*

The first day of the month brings professional developments for many and probably finds you in a very innovative frame of mind. You should now be able to get your head round matters that could have been quite confusing before and will probably kick yourself for not having more savvy previously.

2 SATURDAY ☿ *Moon Age Day 11 Moon Sign Capricorn*

The planetary emphasis right now is on your sense of personal security. All in all, this fact might make the day seem somewhat dull but you need to make changes whenever you can. However, your chart also indicates that you might spend much of the latter part of the day attempting to come to terms with a wayward family member.

3 SUNDAY ☿ *Moon Age Day 12 Moon Sign Aquarius*

The lunar high takes you out of yourself and improves your ability to handle several different tasks at the same time. Now you want to be the life and soul of any party – including some you are planning yourself. Lady Luck is on your side, though you would still be well advised not to speculate too much.

4 MONDAY ☿ *Moon Age Day 13 Moon Sign Aquarius*

This is a period of high energy and maximum demands, most of which you are making of yourself. Don't worry, you are equal to the task and will definitely turn heads wherever you go. Avoid getting tied down with the minutiae of life because it is the overall picture that appeals to you the most now.

5 TUESDAY ☿ *Moon Age Day 14 Moon Sign Aquarius*

Personal matters take on a new and important perspective during the third day of your lunar high this month. It appears that your level of popularity is at maximum and new romantic encounters certainly cannot be ruled out. Your strength of character shows in practically everything you do today.

6 WEDNESDAY ☿ *Moon Age Day 15 Moon Sign Pisces*

It seems as though you are retreating somewhat from the more frenetic qualities of life, but this is only a temporary phase. With all to play for socially and romantically, you will want to drop the traces of responsibility in order to enjoy yourself more. This interlude will definitely do you good.

7 THURSDAY ☿ *Moon Age Day 16   Moon Sign Pisces*

The more determined edge to your nature returns in no uncertain terms. When it comes to getting things right first time, you should have no problem at all. Your confidence is on the increase again and is assisted by the present position of the Sun in your solar eighth house. This is still a transitional period for you.

8 FRIDAY ☿ *Moon Age Day 17   Moon Sign Aries*

Minor financial gains are possible, though probably as a result of your own efforts rather than thanks to general good luck. Once again you discover that having made a decision, you are inclined to stick to it, even at the expense of common sense. Doing things your own way is more or less an art form for Aquarius now.

9 SATURDAY ☿ *Moon Age Day 18   Moon Sign Aries*

Present planetary trends bring out the detective in you. Finding out what makes people tick is especially interesting at the moment, though you need to be somewhat careful because you don't want to be accused of prying into people's lives. Your creative potential is going off the scale, especially regarding changes at home.

10 SUNDAY ☿ *Moon Age Day 19   Moon Sign Taurus*

Most of the changes occurring in your personal life at present come because you are specifically looking for them. This is a time when it is necessary to look at old matters in a very new light. All the same you might be left with the overall impression that you are tinkering with life, rather than shaking it up totally.

11 MONDAY ☿ *Moon Age Day 20   Moon Sign Taurus*

Now you are able to catch up on unfinished business. This Monday allows you more time to please yourself and brings an innovative way of looking at things. Concern for the underdog is present, as it often is, and you are especially good at sorting out the needs and wants of younger family members. Your confidence is on the increase, too.

12 TUESDAY ☿ *Moon Age Day 21   Moon Sign Gemini*

Planetary trends suggest that your life now contains elements of the weird and wonderful. Bearing in mind what Aquarius is like for much of the time it is slightly hard to know how you would recognise the difference. All the same, put yourself in the path of new experiences and don't take anything at face value.

13 WEDNESDAY
Moon Age Day 22   Moon Sign Gemini

With travel matters positively highlighted, you should be happily on the go and probably feeling rather less stressed than might have been the case of late. Although you have been enjoying life to the full, you may have been putting yourself through the mill too much. Now you can relax more, which has to be good.

14 THURSDAY
Moon Age Day 23   Moon Sign Cancer

This is another good day for enjoying the great sense of personal freedom that surrounds you at present. Travel takes on an importance that could extend into your professional life, though moving about for its own sake can be fun too. Avoid arguing with people who clearly know what they are talking about.

15 FRIDAY
Moon Age Day 24   Moon Sign Cancer

Financially speaking you should find the support you need, when it is most required. What seems like a backward step in some ways could prove to be necessary in a practical sense. Maybe you are starting to realise that new and innovative ideas are not always exactly what you need and sometimes there is security in the familiar.

16 SATURDAY
Moon Age Day 25   Moon Sign Cancer

Professional obligations could test your patience if you are a weekend worker. If not, find ways to enjoy yourself beyond the confines of your own front door. The world looks inviting and you should not be short of ideas when it comes to innovation. In this mood, people should find you good to have around and enjoy your company.

17 SUNDAY
Moon Age Day 26   Moon Sign Leo

There isn't a great deal in the way of assistance today and so you might feel you are going it alone. Try to remember that part of what is happening is related to your emotional state, which in turn responds to the lunar low. Slow and steady wins the race, even if this particular lap is not too eventful.

18 MONDAY
Moon Age Day 27   Moon Sign Leo

This might be another day during which you cannot make the sort of headway you would wish, though for some reason you could feel it doesn't matter much. Certainly you can enjoy yourself and having a good time is as important as getting on in life. Friends should prove to be supportive.

19 TUESDAY
Moon Age Day 28   Moon Sign Virgo

This might be a good time to look at the way your life is structured and a period for making necessary changes. It's late in the year for a spring clean but that is more or less what seems to be happening. Don't keep hold of anything simply for the sake of habit. You may have to be slightly ruthless.

20 WEDNESDAY
Moon Age Day 0   Moon Sign Virgo

If you have any problems today, turn on your intuition and see what it is telling you. It should be quite easy to understand what makes other people tick and you can force some real gains as a result. You are very sympathetic to others at present and would be quite willing to change your own direction in life a little in order to help someone else.

21 THURSDAY
Moon Age Day 1   Moon Sign Libra

You could do a lot worse today than spreading your wings. Travel hasn't been uppermost in the mind of Aquarians as much this year as sometimes turns out to be the case, though wanderlust does begin to play a part in your thinking from now on. This would be an ideal time to take an autumn holiday if you can, especially for some late sun.

22 FRIDAY
Moon Age Day 2   Moon Sign Libra

Pressures can come thick and fast at work, though you should be able to dismiss most of them with a shrug. Even when you have managed to climb a series of mountains to get what you want from life, further peaks are in view. It is possible you are trying just a little too hard and that you would benefit from a reduction in pace.

23 SATURDAY
Moon Age Day 3   Moon Sign Scorpio

Once again, you discover a period of change coming upon you. It is possible that one or two friendships have run their course. You don't want to hurt anyone, so you simply retreat from situations you now find boring. Some sort of explanation may be called for, even if you have to bend the truth slightly.

24 SUNDAY
Moon Age Day 4   Moon Sign Scorpio

Emotional matters tend to get quite intense today and you should take great care not to become involved in any arguments. It might appear that people you are usually close to are singularly failing to understand or fall in line with your point of view. A dollop of respect all round seems to be necessary.

25 MONDAY
Moon Age Day 5   Moon Sign Scorpio

Get out and about if you can, the further the better. You are still quieter than usual but trends suggest that you will fare well if you visit places you haven't seen before. Likewise, you may find strangers easier to get along with then people you have known for a long time. This may also be a period for puzzles of one sort or another.

26 TUESDAY
Moon Age Day 6   Moon Sign Sagittarius

Financial matters could make life seem very secure. There is more cash about than would often be the case, some of it likely to come from rather unexpected directions. Conforming to expectations could be rather difficult and you won't relish routine tasks, which you see as being very boring at present.

27 WEDNESDAY
Moon Age Day 7   Moon Sign Sagittarius

The pace of everyday events goes up a notch or two and you should find some exciting events coming along, even if you have to manufacture at least some of these yourself. Your mind is dragged towards the past, either by events or individuals you haven't seen for ages.

28 THURSDAY
Moon Age Day 8   Moon Sign Capricorn

This would make a fine period for pleasure trips and tends to be quite a nostalgic time too, when you enjoy looking back to the past with rose-tinted spectacles. In terms of your working life, you may be able to close a circle in some way and it does look as if new starts with alternative responsibilities are coming along for many Aquarians.

29 FRIDAY
Moon Age Day 9   Moon Sign Capricorn

Hopeful news could easily be coming from far off places. Any Aquarian who has been looking forward to a long journey may not have to wait much longer. There are gains to be made by listening carefully to family members, some of whom are coming up with extremely good ideas at present.

30 SATURDAY
Moon Age Day 10   Moon Sign Capricorn

Social matters could be somewhat hectic today, though you do stand the chance of stumbling across enjoyable situations, possibly without planning any of them. This would not be a good time to get involved in arguments, especially those that crop up in your family or immediate friendship circle so keep away from contentious issues.

October
2017

YOUR MONTH AT A GLANCE

⊕ = Opportunities are around ⊖ = Be on the defensive ⬤ = Life is pretty ordinary

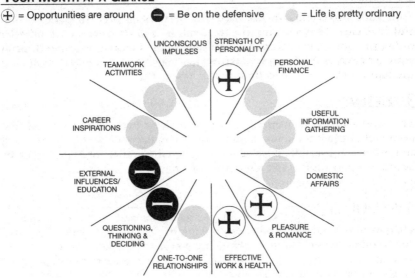

OCTOBER HIGHS AND LOWS

Here I show you how the rhythms of the Moon will affect you this month. Like the tide, your energies and abilities will rise and fall with its pattern. When it is above the centre line, go for it, when it is below, you should be resting.

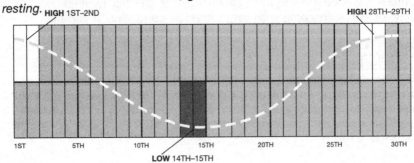

1 SUNDAY
Moon Age Day 11   Moon Sign Aquarius

Mundane issues are apt to get in the way of personal freedom, so it would be just as well to make sure that your point of view is still being heard and that you don't allow the steady pace of your regular life to obscure specific issues which may be on the rise. Romance is likely to be on the cards for some Aquarians at this point in time.

2 MONDAY
Moon Age Day 12   Moon Sign Aquarius

Your ability to communicate with others is favourably highlighted now and it is clear that you intend to speak to as many people as possible today in your efforts to get ahead generally. There are few barriers in your way when it comes to getting your message across intact and, in the main, others want to help you if they can.

3 TUESDAY
Moon Age Day 13   Moon Sign Pisces

The 'work hard and play hard' ethos of your sign is definitely on display right now. Concentrate on those matters that are really important to your future and, whenever possible, integrate your career and social life. There ought to be ample opportunity once again to make an extremely good impression on all kinds of different people.

4 WEDNESDAY
Moon Age Day 14   Moon Sign Pisces

There could be a few obstacles today, particularly at work, most of which are due to differences of opinion between yourself and others. It would be wise to address these as quickly as possible and not to allow technical problems to get out of hand either. Although you stick to your guns today, you might have a tendency to do so too much.

5 THURSDAY
Moon Age Day 15   Moon Sign Aries

A few technical matters have to be ignored today if you want to get ahead quickly. Of course, it would be madness not to pay attention to safety issues and you realise this very well. It is red tape that bothers you most of all – but the signs are that you might have discovered ways to do something about it.

6 FRIDAY
Moon Age Day 16   Moon Sign Aries

In relationships, personal issues may surface, especially if someone thinks you have wronged them in the past. It's time to lay your cards on the table, but this time with some considerable care. In practical matters it is possible to have the penny and the bun right now, but once again you will need to be canny.

7 SATURDAY
Moon Age Day 17   Moon Sign Taurus

The weekend brings a state of affairs that shows little self-control on your part. However, an ill-disciplined approach to situations that you are involved in is not going to help anything at this time. On the contrary, if you don't keep a close eye on circumstances generally, a few of them are likely to run out of control.

8 SUNDAY
Moon Age Day 18   Moon Sign Taurus

There is a strong emphasis on communication today, and specifically on coming to terms with younger people. They might think they have all the answers and so there is no point in trying to bulldoze them with your own point of view. Lead by example, show patience, and all should eventually be well.

9 MONDAY
Moon Age Day 19   Moon Sign Taurus

A few irritations appear to be more or less inevitable at the moment, and generally speaking these are likely to come from the direction of relatives or friends. Don't allow these to subvert your own plans and treat little issues to a dose of common sense. It is the wider spectrum of life that you should address right now.

10 TUESDAY
Moon Age Day 20   Moon Sign Gemini

Today introduces an opportunity to broaden your horizons in ways that you may not have thought of before. Grasp any nettle firmly and take the chance to push your influence with others. If you have some grandiose new scheme it is definitely time to get others on your side and you have the skills to do so.

11 WEDNESDAY
Moon Age Day 21   Moon Sign Gemini

Although you cannot please all of the people, all of the time, there's a good chance you get close to doing so. The fact is that you are as charming as can be right now, something that others could hardly fail to register. Some jobs will take a good deal longer than you expected but it is simply a matter of carrying on steadily.

12 THURSDAY
Moon Age Day 22   Moon Sign Cancer

There are some potentially lucrative ideas around now, most of which you take on board easily and instinctively. Getting others to go along with you won't be easy, particularly if you have failed to think matters through as carefully as you should have. In at least one respect you can expect a breakthrough.

13 FRIDAY
Moon Age Day 23   Moon Sign Cancer

Getting down to brass tacks in your conversations with other people is absolutely vital at this time. There is absolutely no point at the moment in being so diplomatic that those around you fail to understand completely what you are trying to say. Fortunately, there is a middle path that you can usually locate.

14 SATURDAY
Moon Age Day 24   Moon Sign Leo

Getting ahead quite as easily as you may wish isn't going to be easy with the lunar low around. Why try? This Saturday offers you the perfect opportunity to sit and watch life go by for a while. You will feel much better if you take a break and will be better equipped to make use of favourable trends later in the coming week.

15 SUNDAY
Moon Age Day 25   Moon Sign Leo

This is not necessarily a period of self-gain, it really depends on the way you approach specific situations. Go slow and steady, weighing up the pros and cons in each case. The more carefully you address details, the greater is the likelihood of success in the end.

16 MONDAY
Moon Age Day 26   Moon Sign Virgo

You may need the bright lights of the social world to cheer you up today. There are a number of astrological reasons to explain why you are slightly down in the dumps, though there is no real reason to let these spoil your day. Keep in the mainstream at work and avoid unnecessary controversy.

17 TUESDAY
Moon Age Day 27   Moon Sign Virgo

Some skilful manoeuvring may be necessary if you want to avoid family members falling out with each other. Although you won't necessarily make much material progress today, your ability to sort out the problems of those around you should be pleasing enough in its own right.

18 WEDNESDAY
Moon Age Day 28   Moon Sign Libra

This is a good day to be on the move and to be saying what you think, especially about practical situations. The real gains in today might well be romantic. New attachments should be working well under prevailing trends, whilst established ones seem to have new zest and vitality that you are bringing to them.

19 THURSDAY
Moon Age Day 29   Moon Sign Libra

The best advice that can be offered to Aquarius today is to ensure that you get one task out of the way before you start on another. There is a danger of overlap and confusion that you could so easily avoid. Trends do suggest, though, that there ought to be a good deal of happiness about in a family and friendship sense.

20 FRIDAY
Moon Age Day 0   Moon Sign Libra

All joint financial matters are especially well-starred at present, likewise partnerships with a monetary aspect to them. In addition, you should find it easier to whisper those intimate little words that can make all the difference in the relationship stakes. Don't be too quick to jump to conclusions in work matters.

21 SATURDAY
Moon Age Day 1   Moon Sign Scorpio

Improved communication is likely to be the best gift of the weekend. Don't be tardy when it comes to expressing an opinion, even when you know there are people around who will not agree with you. Although you won't be feeling absolutely positive about everything, you can fool others and even yourself in the end.

22 SUNDAY
Moon Age Day 2   Moon Sign Scorpio

There is now a greater emphasis on professional issues, despite the fact that you probably won't even be at work right now. Planning ahead is essential and it would certainly not be advisable to leave anything until the last minute. If you feel you are running out of steam in some way, enlist a little positive support.

23 MONDAY
Moon Age Day 3   Moon Sign Sagittarius

There are certain signposts to success around now, even if you have to keep your eyes wide open in order to recognise them. Socially speaking, you are anxious to meet new people and may well give some of your associations from the past the order of the boot. Aquarius is all about change and diversity at present.

24 TUESDAY
Moon Age Day 4   Moon Sign Sagittarius

You could find the opinions of other to be either irrelevant or perhaps downright annoying now. It is important not to react too strongly so keep your cool. It is possible for you to score some singular successes, simply by refusing to rise to any bait that is presently offered and sticking to what you know to be right.

25 WEDNESDAY
Moon Age Day 5   Moon Sign Sagittarius

Career matters should now be looking good. If you are in full time education, expect some good marks and compliments from tutors. Home-based activities could be slightly less than appealing, though you might have to turn your mind in that direction, if only to please your loved ones.

26 THURSDAY
Moon Age Day 6   Moon Sign Capricorn

Your mind seems to be much more focused and the ability to see the most distant horizon in your life should be a piece of cake. Trends suggest that you can expect a little frustration arising from people who do things without checking, which could lead to a few problems for you further down the line.

27 FRIDAY
Moon Age Day 7   Moon Sign Capricorn

Don't be dissuaded from doing things your own way. If you put yourself out too much to accommodate the ideas of others, no matter how close they may be, you could be in for a loss of some sort. When your intuition tells you to take a specific course of action, it would be sensible to heed it.

28 SATURDAY
Moon Age Day 8   Moon Sign Aquarius

Planetary benefits come along from a number of different directions whilst the lunar high is present. You can afford to back your hunches and might find yourself sought out by someone you think of as being extremely special. Although the summer has now definitely gone you may decide to spend time out of doors.

29 SUNDAY
Moon Age Day 9   Moon Sign Aquarius

Plans should be turning out more or less as you would expect, leaving you with hours on your hands that can be simply used for having fun. There are some particularly interesting people around, one or two of whom have had their eyes on you for a while. Affection comes from some very surprising directions.

30 MONDAY
Moon Age Day 10   Moon Sign Pisces

The potential for getting what you want in almost any area of life is strong today. There are people around who actively want to offer you help and support and you should be able to locate them easily enough. Conforming to the expectations that older relatives have of you could be somewhat complicated.

31 TUESDAY

Moon Age Day 11 Moon Sign Pisces

In debates or discussions, you are clearly up against people with strong egos at the moment. However, remember that there is more than one way to skin a cat. If you remain absolutely charming and don't rise to the bait, you will get your own way by default. Aquarius can be extremely cunning on occasions.

November

2017

YOUR MONTH AT A GLANCE

$\oplus$ = Opportunities are around   ⬤ = Be on the defensive   ⬤ = Life is pretty ordinary

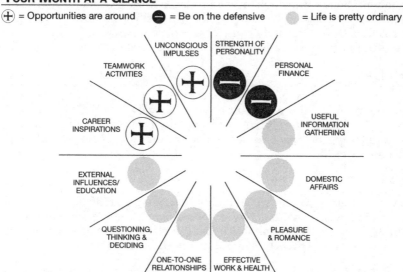

NOVEMBER HIGHS AND LOWS

Here I show you how the rhythms of the Moon will affect you this month. Like the tide, your energies and abilities will rise and fall with its pattern. When it is above the centre line, go for it, when it is below, you should be resting.

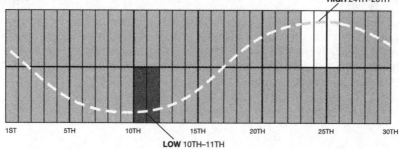

HIGH 24TH–26TH

LOW 10TH–11TH

111

1 WEDNESDAY
Moon Age Day 12   Moon Sign Pisces

The progressive trends you have been experiencing for a while now tend to continue, bringing you more influence and a greater degree of control over the circumstances of your own life. Friends should be especially helpful today and might even assist you in the direction of a much-cherished ambition.

2 THURSDAY
Moon Age Day 13   Moon Sign Aries

Communications with people in the professional world could suffer a little today, maybe because you are not quite as friendly as has been the case in the recent past. In some ways you seek to isolate yourself and could even be somewhat prickly if you feel yourself threatened or undermined in any way.

3 FRIDAY
Moon Age Day 14   Moon Sign Aries

This is another day on which your personal influence may be hampered in a number of different ways. Don't be afraid to allow yourself to show some vulnerability because this merely makes you look all the more human when viewed through the eyes of other people. You have a lot on your plate, so take things steadily.

4 SATURDAY
Moon Age Day 15   Moon Sign Taurus

Now is the time to be yourself and to make room in your life for a few small, personal indulgences. Although you are still going to be quite active, there ought to be interludes during which you can please yourself and yet manage to help others too. Diversity is important in personal interests.

5 SUNDAY
Moon Age Day 16   Moon Sign Taurus

A fast pace of events in the social world is to be expected today. There won't always be time to pick your words quite as carefully as you might wish and so it is extra important to at least try to think before you speak. The only danger here is that you will offer offence when none was intended.

6 MONDAY
Moon Age Day 17   Moon Sign Gemini

You should not have to go it alone today. It appears that there are many people who will lend a hand when you need it the most. If you do find yourself isolated, the fault could be your own. There are occasions when Aquarius shows itself to be too proud for its own good and today might be an example of this.

7 TUESDAY
Moon Age Day 18   Moon Sign Gemini

Socially speaking, this continues to be a very fulfilling period which may offer you the chance to get on-side with people who haven't played a significant role in your life up to now. Relatives and friends alike might have plans for next weekend but you might be inclined to want to keep your options open.

8 WEDNESDAY
Moon Age Day 19   Moon Sign Cancer

A socially motivated period continues, though of course that isn't at all strange for your zodiac sign, so you may not even take too much notice of it. Whispering words of love into the right ear could prove interesting today and will show your partner how you really feel during a busy period.

9 THURSDAY
Moon Age Day 20   Moon Sign Cancer

Get as much done as you can early in the day because later on there are social trends calling out to you. The weekend is already in view and you could have yourself a fine old time in the evening. Love plays a significant part in your thinking and you could be spending a significant amount of time with family members.

10 FRIDAY
Moon Age Day 21   Moon Sign Leo

The lunar low brings a planetary lull, just in time for Friday morning. The bearing this has on your life really depends on your attitude. As long as you are willing to take comfort in small things, and can shelve some of your most grandiose schemes for just a couple of days, all should be well.

11 SATURDAY
Moon Age Day 22   Moon Sign Leo

Today is a day to settle for smaller, less demanding plans. Saturday should bring feelings of peace and contentment, together with a willingness to listen to what other people are saying. If you make the most of this opportunity, you could find that the lunar low this time around has turned out to be a blessing in disguise.

12 SUNDAY
Moon Age Day 23   Moon Sign Virgo

A sense of freedom is vitally important now and you won't take kindly to being thwarted when you really feel that you need to get your own way. Travel could be uppermost in your mind and it is clear that you have a particular vision regarding the future. A degree of compromise is called for, but not too much.

13 MONDAY
Moon Age Day 24   Moon Sign Virgo

Loved ones and intimates require careful handling today. If there are sensitive issues to deal with your jokey sense of humour may not be appropriate and you may need to exercise a degree of patience, especially with people whose thought processes are not as quick as your own. Create some interesting interludes for family members.

14 TUESDAY
Moon Age Day 25   Moon Sign Libra

Although you could be rather impatient with material obligations today, you will have to get these out of the way before you can begin to move forward in certain respects. It isn't so much what people need of you that can irritate, more what some of them expect. It is very important to keep your cool.

15 WEDNESDAY
Moon Age Day 26   Moon Sign Libra

Being on the move can be quite rewarding. This is certainly not a time to be standing still or to allow the grass to grow under your feet with regard to exciting new plans. You will be amazed just how much work you can get through right now, some of which is ably assisted by friends.

16 THURSDAY
Moon Age Day 27   Moon Sign Libra

The emphasis today is on life's more playful aspects. It might be hard to take anything particularly seriously, at least for a day or two. However, your offbeat sense of humour and off-the-wall attitude will be popular with almost everyone and may actually lead to you achieving a great deal.

17 FRIDAY
Moon Age Day 28   Moon Sign Scorpio

Be careful when it comes to listening to gossip. There is a good chance that much of what you hear today is either misleading or downright wrong. Opt for some fresh-air if you can. At this point in time locking yourself inside the house won't be good for you, mentally or physically.

18 SATURDAY
Moon Age Day 0   Moon Sign Scorpio

This is a particularly good time for any involvement in intellectual interests or philosophical investigation. All Aquarians want to know what makes the world the way it is and speculation is very healthy for you. Of course, you won't get all the answers to the world's problems, but you can have fun trying.

19 SUNDAY
Moon Age Day 1   Moon Sign Sagittarius

Though some obstacles may get in the way if you are at work, socially and romantically, you appear to be on top form. Consideration for family members and friends comes as second nature, though you won't always be able to help them quite to the extent you might wish. The generally progressive phase continues.

20 MONDAY
Moon Age Day 2   Moon Sign Sagittarius

You could be rather socially reluctant today, which might not appear to bode well for a new week. Take comfort from the fact that this concern is probably groundless. You are likely to be very good when mixing with people you know well and your degree of reserve will be restricted to the times when you have to deal with those you don't know so well.

21 TUESDAY
Moon Age Day 3   Moon Sign Sagittarius

This is a day to broaden your mind. There are a few complications possible but each of them teaches you something more about life and the best way to live it. Boredom is unlikely and it appears that you will find newer and better ways to show both your affection and genuine concern for others.

22 WEDNESDAY
Moon Age Day 4   Moon Sign Capricorn

The instinct for skilful money-making is strong at the moment. There are ways and means to bring more cash into your life and you will recognise most of them. Although you could find the going a little tough in terms of casual friendships, the people who love you the most won't let you down.

23 THURSDAY
Moon Age Day 5   Moon Sign Capricorn

It looks as though professional matters are well-starred at the moment, even if it doesn't seem to be that way at first. When you are faced with awkward people today, turn on that natural charm and watch situations change quickly. Prepare to have to show a good deal of give and take in romantic attachments.

24 FRIDAY
Moon Age Day 6   Moon Sign Aquarius

The lunar high finds you fighting fit and anxious to make the best sort of impression. If there is any fly in the ointment at all, it could be that not everyone you come across is equally helpful. Put your best foot forward at work but leave time for personal enjoyment coming your way later in the day.

25 SATURDAY
Moon Age Day 7   Moon Sign Aquarius

The go-ahead influence continues and you find people rather more willing to live with your suggestions now. Part of the reason for this is your persuasive tongue and you won't have much trouble bringing people round to your point of view. Romance is especially well highlighted for those on the lookout for love.

26 SUNDAY
Moon Age Day 8   Moon Sign Aquarius

Your more charming and playful side is now clearly on display. Don't be too distracted by the fun and games that are available because there is plenty for you to do in practical sense. Trends suggest that many Aquarians will now be looking at the possibility of making changes to their living environments.

27 MONDAY
Moon Age Day 9   Moon Sign Pisces

Work and professional matters should prove more than fulfilling. Even if you don't have to toil professionally today, you will find something to keep you occupied. Physical activity is very good for you, as long as you don't do the usual Air-sign trick and overdo it. Moderation in all things is the key.

28 TUESDAY
Moon Age Day 10   Moon Sign Pisces

Challenges are likely, as are confrontations because now you are not likely to be willing to sit back and watch others lord it over you. On the contrary, you are not only competitive at present but also probably more than willing to defend yourself before you have even been attacked. Learn how to take a breath and count to ten before you act.

29 WEDNESDAY
Moon Age Day 11   Moon Sign Aries

The focus now shifts to the social arena. If there are any invitations on offer today, grab them with both hands. You need the support of friends and relatives if you are going to get the very best out of any given situation. What you definitely don't need is to be nagged, so stay away from people who insist on moaning about anything you do.

30 THURSDAY
Moon Age Day 12   Moon Sign Aries

If you find yourself under any pressure today, it is likely to come from the direction of people who could be a little jealous of you. Take this situation in your stride because this is definitely not a day to give as good as you get. By remaining composed, you will win the battle in the end.

December
2017

YOUR MONTH AT A GLANCE

$\oplus$ = Opportunities are around ● = Be on the defensive ● = Life is pretty ordinary

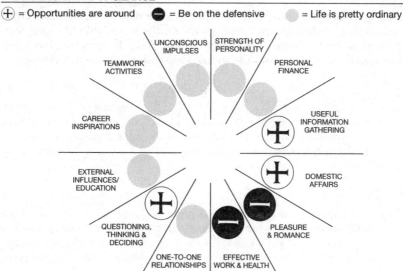

- UNCONSCIOUS IMPULSES
- STRENGTH OF PERSONALITY
- TEAMWORK ACTIVITIES
- PERSONAL FINANCE
- CAREER INSPIRATIONS
- USEFUL INFORMATION GATHERING
- EXTERNAL INFLUENCES/ EDUCATION
- DOMESTIC AFFAIRS
- QUESTIONING, THINKING & DECIDING
- PLEASURE & ROMANCE
- ONE-TO-ONE RELATIONSHIPS
- EFFECTIVE WORK & HEALTH

DECEMBER HIGHS AND LOWS

Here I show you how the rhythms of the Moon will affect you this month. Like the tide, your energies and abilities will rise and fall with its pattern. When it is above the centre line, go for it, when it is below, you should be resting.

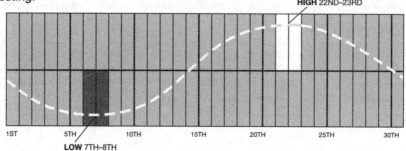

HIGH 22ND–23RD

1ST 5TH 10TH 15TH 20TH 25TH 30TH

LOW 7TH–8TH

I FRIDAY
Moon Age Day 13   Moon Sign Taurus

It's the first day of December and you won't want to let any opportunity pass you by at this time. From a social point of view the day should be very enjoyable as you know what you want from new encounters. Don't be slow to ask for a favour, particularly from people who are always willing to lend a hand.

2 SATURDAY
Moon Age Day 14   Moon Sign Taurus

Your go-getting side is certainly on display at present. With masses of energy, an original way of seeing things and plenty of charm, you should have little difficulty impressing some pretty important people. Although a good time socially speaking, today revolves primarily around work and practical issues.

3 SUNDAY   ☿
Moon Age Day 15   Moon Sign Gemini

Personal indulgences would be good today but there isn't really all that much time to enjoy them. You should be able to succeed, perhaps even against some very formidable odds. In a way, the more difficult situations are the better you like them right now. Avoid routines or anything dull that holds little interest for you at present.

4 MONDAY   ☿
Moon Age Day 16   Moon Sign Gemini

Though your love life might not be offering everything you would wish, it is possible to pep things up with just a little effort on your part. Any minor health problems should become less of a concern now, particularly since you are willing to take things easily, and perhaps even delegate some responsibilities.

5 TUESDAY   ☿
Moon Age Day 17   Moon Sign Cancer

When it comes to matters associated with money it appears that your rather happy-go-lucky nature isn't so useful at present. Trends suggest that you need to count the pennies carefully, making certain that you are not taking financial risks or spending needlessly on luxuries you don't even really want.

6 WEDNESDAY   ☿
Moon Age Day 18   Moon Sign Cancer

There should be a greater sense of adventure showing itself today, which is something of a pity bearing in mind that the month's lunar low begins tomorrow. For the moment, push forward progressively and embrace change. Relationships ought to be working especially well at the moment.

7 THURSDAY ☿ *Moon Age Day 19   Moon Sign Leo*

A rest period is called for, and today offers all the right circumstances to get one. Don't rush your fences and be willing to allow others to take some of the strain. You should find that you have friends who care about you deeply, as well as relatives who are quite willing to put themselves out on your account.

8 FRIDAY ☿ *Moon Age Day 20   Moon Sign Leo*

Although the lull patch is still in operation, things ought to speed up noticeably towards the middle of the day. That old friend of yours, wanderlust, begins to play a part in your thinking and you won't take kindly to be being trapped in situations you see as being distinctly boring.

9 SATURDAY ☿ *Moon Age Day 21   Moon Sign Virgo*

Encounters with people who come new into your life could prove to be something of an inspiration now. Someone, somewhere seeks to offer you some timely advice and it would be at least sensible to listen, even if you decide to follow your own path in any case. Trends move on and all in all, this should be a positive day.

10 SUNDAY ☿ *Moon Age Day 22   Moon Sign Virgo*

Simple conversation is what proves to be most useful today. The things you hear as you move about from place to place could inspire you in some way and might lead to ideas that can mature in the fullness of time. Although you can be of tremendous use to friends, there are some things you cannot do for them.

11 MONDAY ☿ *Moon Age Day 23   Moon Sign Virgo*

Relationships might be something of a struggle to deal with at the beginning of this working week. In games of chance or sporting activities you clearly have your wits about you and might enjoy some successful results. Don't gloat over your achievements, though. It isn't necessary and only cheapens your winning streak.

12 THURSDAY ☿ *Moon Age Day 24   Moon Sign Libra*

An important plan could miss the target unless you make absolutely sure of all the details. It can't be stressed enough now how important it is to check and double-check. If you are careful, something you have wanted for ages could be coming your way at any time now, but if you are sloppy you may be disappointed.

13 WEDNESDAY ☿   *Moon Age Day 25   Moon Sign Libra*

Professionally speaking, the present position of the Moon brings a more stable and easy-to-read phase. Contributing to your own eventual success isn't difficult, even though you have half an eye on the festive period that lies before you. Confidence is strong when you are dealing with matters you understand.

14 THURSDAY ☿   *Moon Age Day 26   Moon Sign Scorpio*

Your social life is still on a roll and it looks as though some Aquarians will be starting Christmas very early this year. Give yourself time to take in something that is both interesting and educational and don't rush your fences where new skills are concerned. Most important of all, realise how close the holidays are.

15 FRIDAY ☿   *Moon Age Day 27   Moon Sign Scorpio*

You are best suited to working alone for the moment. This does not mean you are antisocial in any way but merely that you know what needs to be done and how to go about it. Once the responsibilities of the day are over, you should be pleased to mix freely and to be as co-operative as is necessary.

16 SATURDAY ☿   *Moon Age Day 28   Moon Sign Scorpio*

Put all thoughts of work behind you if you are an Aquarian who has the weekend to yourself. Now comes a time when you can think specifically about romance and the social side of life. This might be just about the first time that you have realised that Christmas is just around the corner and if so, make the most of the opportunities the season offers.

17 SUNDAY ☿   *Moon Age Day 29   Moon Sign Sagittarius*

Although there are plenty of people around you at the moment, this is one of those days when you are inclined to make decisions more or less independently. This does not mean locking yourself away in a darkened room for hours at a stretch, but present trends do indicate that you may not be susceptible to the influence of others.

18 MONDAY ☿   *Moon Age Day 0   Moon Sign Sagittarius*

Gradually, you find yourself identifying more with the needs and aspirations of the group and that means as the month wears on any recent solitary tendencies are inclined to disappear. The quirky side of Aquarius begins to show more, though in ways that make your relatives and friends smile.

19 TUESDAY ☿ *Moon Age Day 1   Moon Sign Capricorn*

Your general manner is somewhat blunter today than might be expected for Aquarius and you should exercise a good deal of patience when dealing with people who are naturally inclined to get on your nerves. You can easily use present trends to get ahead, though you probably also really need to lighten up somewhat.

20 WEDNESDAY ☿ *Moon Age Day 2   Moon Sign Capricorn*

Today you can expect an increase in all pleasurable endeavours. It's amazing where all your present energy is coming from and you should be enjoying life to the full. New and better possibilities at work might come about as a result of someone else's slightly bad luck but you can't blame yourself for that eventuality.

21 THURSDAY ☿ *Moon Age Day 3   Moon Sign Capricorn*

This is a day on which it would be wise to follow your instincts, which are unlikely to let you down. Although not everyone you meet at present is equally reliable, it ought to be fairly easy for you to sort out the wheat from the chaff. Turn up your intuition and listen carefully to what it is telling you.

22 FRIDAY ☿ *Moon Age Day 4   Moon Sign Aquarius*

Now the lunar high is really on your side, making the run-up to Christmas perhaps the best interlude during December. Give and take in family matters is noticed and gains you some important allies. Affairs of the heart are positively highlighted and it isn't at all hard to make a good impression.

23 SATURDAY *Moon Age Day 5   Moon Sign Aquarius*

When it comes to voicing your opinions it appears that you are only too willing to have your say. Good fortune is still on your side, but you may tend to push your luck somewhat more than is good for you. Try to curb your enthusiasm just a little and don't be too quick to volunteer for anything.

24 SUNDAY *Moon Age Day 6   Moon Sign Pisces*

Christmas Eve may well set a fast pace and in fact before it is over you could be quite tired. Spread your efforts socially and don't let people monopolise you. The fact is that family and friends deserve at least some of your time, particularly younger people at this special time of the year.

25 MONDAY
Moon Age Day 7   Moon Sign Pisces

There is absolutely no doubt that your typical Aquarian nature can so easily bring out the best in others. You have plenty to keep you busy, both inside the family and further afield. This is unlikely to be a totally stay-at-home sort of Christmas Day for many Aquarians and a little excitement is quite possible.

26 TUESDAY
Moon Age Day 8   Moon Sign Pisces

Your social life generally, and your association with people you love especially, sets today apart as being quite special. There is a quiet side to your nature all the same and you might choose to spend some time watching an old movie or perhaps reading a good book. Don't be surprised if you are very nostalgic today.

27 WEDNESDAY
Moon Age Day 9   Moon Sign Aries

This is a really good time to keep your eyes and ears open. All manner of opportunities are at hand and you don't want to miss any of them. On a cautionary note, though, take what others are saying with a pinch of salt because it is entirely possible they are either joking, or trying to fool you in some way.

28 THURSDAY
Moon Age Day 10   Moon Sign Aries

For some Aquarians there is likely to be a new or renewed romantic interest to think about. Trends suggest that you should be fully committed to having a good time, particularly this evening. A few family responsibilities may crowd in during the day but you will find time later to pop a few more corks.

29 FRIDAY
Moon Age Day 11   Moon Sign Taurus

You can afford to exploit the general good luck that surrounds you at present and it is more or less certain that your organisational skills are well honed for the moment. It appears you are now better at expressing your opinions in ways that others find easier to understand and you are clearly exhibiting your sense of fun.

30 SATURDAY
Moon Age Day 12   Moon Sign Taurus

When it comes to organising your home life, you should be extremely co-operative and anxious to show just how giving you can be. This is in stark contrast to the more decisive qualities you possess. As a result, there could be a few people around who find this polarity difficult to understand and are confused by your present laid-back approach.

31 SUNDAY
Moon Age Day 13   Moon Sign Gemini

New Year's Eve finds you busier than ever and quite happy to take on any number of new responsibilities. You see the year ahead in terms of a wide road that can lead to some exciting places. So positive is your attitude at present that party time tonight is likely to be particularly special, perhaps even quite magical.

How to Calculate Your Rising Sign

Most astrologers agree that, next to the Sun Sign, the most important influence on any person is the Rising Sign at the time of their birth. The Rising Sign represents the astrological sign that was rising over the eastern horizon when each and every one of us came into the world. It is sometimes also called the Ascendant.

Let us suppose, for example, that you were born with the Sun in the zodiac sign of Libra. This would bestow certain characteristics on you that are likely to be shared by all other Librans. However, a Libran with Aries Rising would show a very different attitude towards life, and of course relationships, than a Libran with Pisces Rising.

For these reasons, this book shows how your zodiac Rising Sign has a bearing on all the possible positions of the Sun at birth. Simply look through the Aries table opposite.

As long as you know your approximate time of birth the graph will show you how to discover your Rising Sign.

Look across the top of the graph of your zodiac sign to find your date of birth, and down the side for your birth time (I have used Greenwich Mean Time). Where they cross is your Rising Sign. Don't forget to subtract an hour (or two) if appropriate for Summer Time.

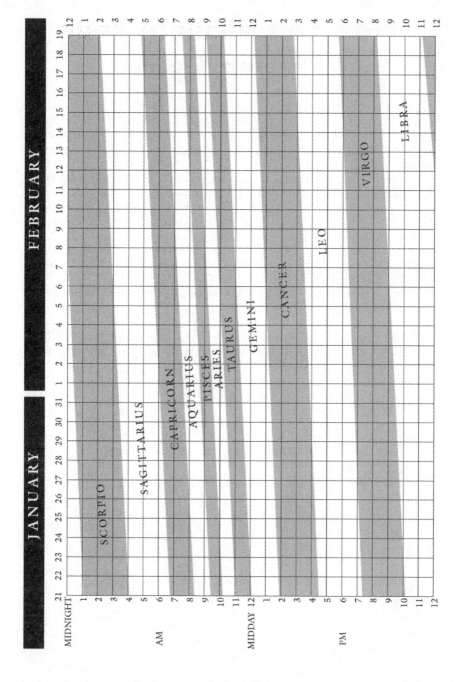

THE ZODIAC, PLANETS AND CORRESPONDENCES

The Earth revolves around the Sun once every calendar year, so when viewed from Earth the Sun appears in a different part of the sky as the year progresses. In astrology, these parts of the sky are divided into the signs of the zodiac and this means that the signs are organised in a circle. The circle begins with Aries and ends with Pisces.

Taking the zodiac sign as a starting point, astrologers then work with all the positions of planets, stars and many other factors to calculate horoscopes and birth charts and tell us what the stars have in store for us.

The table below shows the planets and Elements for each of the signs of the zodiac. Each sign belongs to one of the four Elements: Fire, Air, Earth or Water. Fire signs are creative and enthusiastic; Air signs are mentally active and thoughtful; Earth signs are constructive and practical; Water signs are emotional and have strong feelings.

It also shows the metals and gemstones associated with, or corresponding with, each sign. The correspondence is made when a metal or stone possesses properties that are held in common with a particular sign of the zodiac.

Finally, the table shows the opposite of each star sign – this is the opposite sign in the astrological circle.

Placed	Sign	Symbol	Element	Planet	Metal	Stone	Opposite
1	Aries	Ram	Fire	Mars	Iron	Bloodstone	Libra
2	Taurus	Bull	Earth	Venus	Copper	Sapphire	Scorpio
3	Gemini	Twins	Air	Mercury	Mercury	Tiger's Eye	Sagittarius
4	Cancer	Crab	Water	Moon	Silver	Pearl	Capricorn
5	Leo	Lion	Fire	Sun	Gold	Ruby	Aquarius
6	Virgo	Maiden	Earth	Mercury	Mercury	Sardonyx	Pisces
7	Libra	Scales	Air	Venus	Copper	Sapphire	Aries
8	Scorpio	Scorpion	Water	Pluto	Plutonium	Jasper	Taurus
9	Sagittarius	Archer	Fire	Jupiter	Tin	Topaz	Gemini
10	Capricorn	Goat	Earth	Saturn	Lead	Black Onyx	Cancer
11	Aquarius	Waterbearer	Air	Uranus	Uranium	Amethyst	Leo
12	Pisces	Fishes	Water	Neptune	Tin	Moonstone	Virgo